colour for life

colour for life

emotional, spiritual and physical wellbeing through colour

charles phillips

RYLAND
PETERS
& SMALL

LONDON   NEW YORK

SENIOR EDITOR Henrietta Heald
PICTURE RESEARCH Emily Westlake
PRODUCTION Deborah Wehner, Jacquie Horner
ART DIRECTOR Gabriella Le Grazie
PUBLISHING DIRECTOR Alison Starling

First published in the United Kingdom
in 2004 by Ryland Peters & Small
Kirkman House
12–14 Whitfield Street
London W1T 2RP
www.rylandpeters.com

10 9 8 7 6 5 4 3 2 1

ISBN 1 84172 690 7

A CIP record for this book is available
from the British Library.

Printed in China.

contents

introduction

Every day of our lives we are affected by colour. The decorative scheme in a room can quicken our spirits; the bright shades of sportswear can boost our energy levels; the food colours on our plates at mealtimes can stimulate appetite. Outdoors, a bank of yellow daffodils in a spring garden may touch us with delight, or the reds and oranges of autumnal trees amaze us.

Natural daylight contains the colours of the spectrum that we see displayed in the rainbow that sometimes follows a storm. Our moods and physiological responses are affected by the different combinations of spectrum colours in daylight at various times of the day and in the different seasons of the year. For example, compare your mood in the yellow light of a sunny afternoon with how you feel in the mauve dusk or indigo midnight a few hours later; think of how your energy levels dip as the hours of daylight shorten with the approach of winter, but pick up again with the different colour mix of the longer days of spring.

Colours have a powerful impact, speaking directly to us all on a level deep beneath conscious thought. The colours we choose for our clothing at work and play and for our decorative schemes at home tell other people a great deal about us. Depending on our natural colouring, there are some colours that each of us should avoid; equally, some colours send out messages about us that we may not wish to broadcast. Often the effect is more powerful because it is unspoken.

The language of colour is one we all hear but often cannot speak – we feel its effects without being able to explain them. Nevertheless, as we become attuned to colour we learn to use it to present ourselves and our homes to best advantage. In this book you will find accessible advice on combining colours in your living room or kitchen, on creating a beautiful spread of colours in your garden, on the best colours to wear for an important job interview or dinner date, on the links between food colour and nutritional value, and on the connections between colour and health.

For colour also influences physical, psychological and spiritual vitality. The powerful effects of colour vibrations embrace the body and open doorways to the mind and spirit; they can be used to boost and safeguard physical health and to soothe or enliven the soul. The therapeutic use of coloured gems, colour-vitalized drinks and coloured light derives from time-honoured wisdom that can be traced back at least as far as ancient Egypt and also finds expression in Indian Ayurvedic medicine. Each one of us is unique. Finding and using the right colours for you can enhance your spiritual growth, boost your self-esteem, help you to overcome fears and mental obstacles and unleash your creativity.

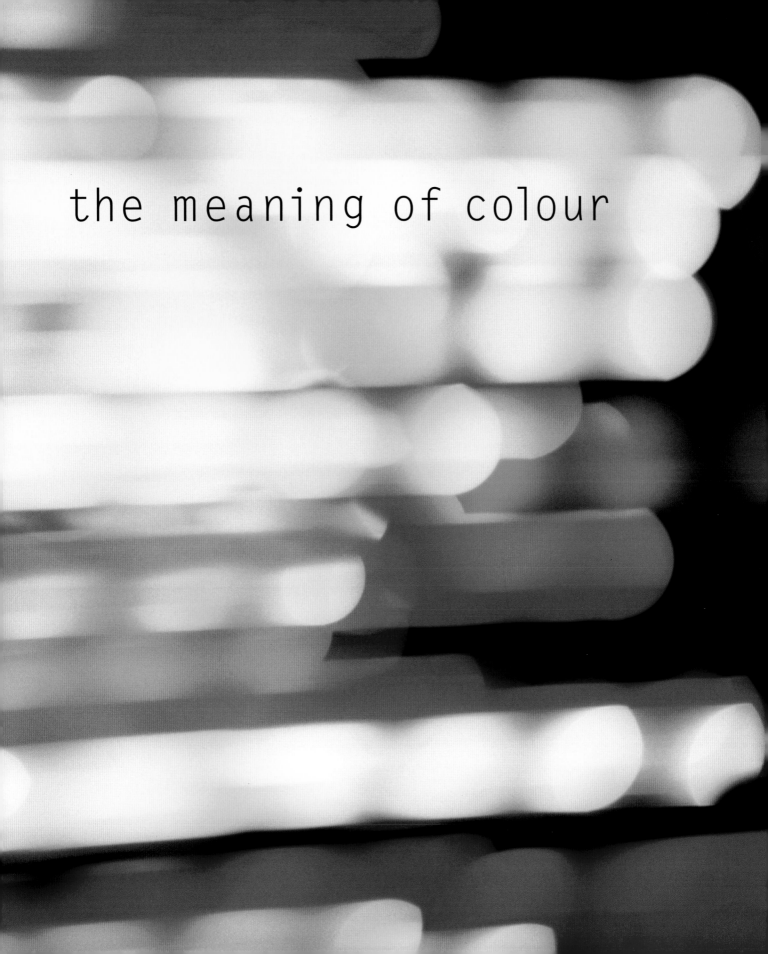

the meaning of colour

light and pigments

You cannot tell your red socks and blue socks apart in a pitch-dark bedroom because you cannot see colour without light. Colour is carried by light. Indeed, colour *is* light. What we perceive as red is light of a particular wavelength and frequency, while blue is light of a different wavelength and frequency. Light and colour are the way humans experience one part of the electromagnetic spectrum.

RAINBOW COLOURS

The rainbow colours are combined in sunlight. In 1666 the English scientist Isaac Newton revealed the constituent colours of sunlight by passing rays through a glass prism and producing the spectrum of colours: red-orange-yellow-green-blue-indigo-violet. The reason why these colours appear in the rainbow after a storm is that droplets of water in the atmosphere function as tiny prisms, splitting the rays of light.

REFLECTED LIGHT

When we see an object in a particular colour, we are registering the wavelength of light that the object reflects. A red chair, for example, absorbs all the wavelengths of visible light except the red ones. A blackboard absorbs all colours, while a brilliant white door reflects all the colours of visible white light. An object will appear to be a different colour under coloured light.

MIXING COLOURS

White light can be split into just three primary colours: red-orange, green and blue-violet. If you train three spotlights in these colours on a theatre stage, you create a white beam. This process is known as additive mixing. The colours in paints and fabrics are made in a different way – by subtractive mixing. In this context the three primary colours are red, blue and yellow. They cannot be made by mixing other colours. When they are combined, the product is black.

ELECTROMAGNETIC RADIATION

HIGH-AMPLITUDE COLOURS

A **bright blue** or **bright yellow** is exciting to the eye — just a small brightly painted area may be sufficient to enliven an entire room, and a small accent such as a buttonhole flower can transform a formal suit.

A colour appears brighter when it is reflected strongly and when it has a tall wavelength (a larger distance between the high point and the low point of the wave). Colours with tall wavelengths are said in the jargon to have 'high amplitude'.

We are bombarded by waves of electromagnetic energy from the sun and other stars, and from terrestrial sources. But visible light is only one-sixtieth of the full range of electromagnetic radiation.

- at one end of the spectrum are **radio** and **television waves**, **microwaves** and **radar waves**, all of which are long waves with a slow frequency of vibration

- at the other end of the spectrum are **gamma waves**, which are short waves vibrating at a fast frequency

- **infrared waves** of light are just too long for humans to see, but can be felt as heat

- the visible colours in sunlight range from **red** (the longest wave we can see) through the other colours of the rainbow – **orange**, **yellow**, **green**, **blue** and **indigo** – to **violet** (the shortest wave we can see)

- just beyond our vision at the short-wave end of the spectrum are **ultraviolet** rays, then x-rays and gamma rays

MYSTIC VISION

According to ancient tradition, mystics of Christian, Hindu and other faiths have seen colours far beyond the normal range when in a state of heightened religious awareness. Such mystics also reportedly see a different quality of light and have a powerfully intense experience of familiar colours such as the yellow of a flower.

Some say they can see the 'aura' of invisible energy that surrounds each one of us (see pages 112–13). Those who live a simple and selfless life, eating moderately and devoting their energies to the welfare of others, are said to develop a bright and unpolluted aura – and for this reason, perhaps, Christ, the Virgin Mary and Christian saints are depicted with a 'halo' of pure light around the head.

how we see colour

People with normal sight can identify colours without conscious effort. The colours in light are distinguished by the retina at the rear of the eye. When light rays enter the eye, they pass through the cornea and then through a watery fluid known as the aqueous humour before reaching the lens. The light rays are focused by the lens onto the retina, where they stimulate two specialized cells – rods and cones.

Rods are highly sensitive to light but not to colour. They can distinguish between shades of grey, white and black, enabling us to make things out in poor light. Cones come in three types, each holding a pigment that absorbs one of the three different wavelengths of light: long wavelength (red/orange), middle wavelength (green) and short wavelength (blue/violet). When it comes into contact with light of the wavelength to which it is sensitive, the pigment breaks down, and this process sends an impulse along the optic nerve on the start of its journey to the brain, where it is interpreted.

If light of more than one wavelength enters the eye, more than one type of cone is stimulated. If you see a man in a yellow shirt, the light rays stimulate a mixture of cones sensitive to red and green light – and the signals sent by the cones deliver a message interpreted by the brain as 'yellow'. People who are colour-blind have abnormal numbers of cones sensitive to particular light wavelengths – so they cannot see those colours as other people do.

'SEEING' COLOURS THROUGH THE SKIN

Some blind people can distinguish between paper or cloth of different colours simply by holding their fingertips or hands above the pieces of material. They can feel the different wavelengths of light through their skin – and report that some colours feel cool while others are warm.

You may be able to train yourself to experience this phenomenon. Take some squares of coloured cloth and lay them on a table. Pass your hands over the squares with your eyes shut. Be sensitive to any differences in energy you can feel. Over many days, perhaps a few weeks, repeat the experiment and see if you can develop an association between types of energy field and particular colours.

WHY GREEN IS THE MOST SOOTHING COLOUR

Green suggests natural light in restful, rural settings, and this association may be enough to make the colour soothing to the spirit. Also, the wavelength of green light is near the middle of the visible spectrum, making it more restful than short- or long-wavelength light.

Think of a rainbow: **violet**, **indigo**, **blue**, **green**, **yellow**, **orange**, **red**. Green is the colour of the centre, and is associated with the heart chakra (see page 112) and feelings of love, peace and security. If you have a nasty shock, you may find yourself drawn to green – try to make time for nature walks, look out a green scarf or hat to wear, or use a green drape somewhere in your home.

the wheel of colours

Colour therapists – who use coloured light and materials for healing – teach that we each have a 'soul colour' that appeals to us very strongly and feeds our spirit. Equally, we all acknowledge colours or colour combinations that do not make us feel good. Indeed, they may 'turn us off', making us feel ill at ease or even physically unwell – perhaps because they recall an unpleasant experience or simply because we do not like their vibrational energy.

In addition to our highly personal colour likes and dislikes, we all share recognition of certain colour combinations that work well and others that clash. The colour wheel is a traditional tool for determining which colours complement one another and which ones are likely to produce a jarring effect.

A colour wheel is made by joining the two ends of the colour spectrum – red and violet – at a point on a circle and running the colours of the spectrum around the circle's circumference. The three primary colours from which all pigments are made – red, yellow and blue – sit at one-third intervals on the circle.

ONE, TWO, THREE

The colour that sits at the halfway point on the circumference between two primaries is known as a secondary colour. The secondary that falls halfway between red and yellow is orange. The other secondary colours are green, halfway between yellow and blue, and violet, the mid-point between blue and red.

The colour that is found halfway between a primary colour and its secondary is called a tertiary colour. The tertiary between yellow (primary) and green (secondary) is a bright lime green.

The colours opposite each another on the colour wheel are called complementaries. The complementary colour to red is green, while orange is complementary to blue, and yellow is complementary to violet. These colours 'attract' one another and can make a pleasing combination in an outfit, a decorative scheme or a bank of flowers. Each colour draws out the richness of the other. Imagine a box of oranges packed in blue tissue – the packaging makes the orange colour of the fruit much more striking.

COLOURS OF LIGHT

The colour wheel described above is based on the colours in pigments and dyes. Healers and colour therapists working with coloured light draw up a different colour wheel built around the three primary colours red/orange, green and blue/violet. On this wheel the complementary of red/orange is turquoise, the complementary of green is magenta, and the complementary of blue/violet is orange/yellow. Coloured light treatments use both a colour and its complementary (see page117).

TYPES OF COLOUR SCHEME

The traditional theory of colours defines several harmonious 'colour schemes' – combinations of colours that look good.

- a **complementary** colour scheme uses opposites on the wheel - for example, **blue** furnishings and accents with **burnt-orange** walls

- a **monochromatic** scheme uses a single colour in many different shades – **dark blue**, **sky blue**, **royal blue** and so on

- an **analogous** scheme uses colours that are adjacent on the wheel – **yellow** with **lime green** or **blue** with **blue-violet**

- an **achromatic** scheme uses **black**, **white**, **silver** and **grey**; it may need enlivening with accents of bright colour from other groups – for example, a minimalist **black-and-white** interior might be improved by a dramatic **red** rug

SEEING THE COMPLEMENTARY

When you stare at a block of a single colour, your eyes produce an 'after-image' of the complementary colour. Try staring intensely at a **red** sweater or teapot for a few moments, then look away at a patch of **white** wall or a piece of blank paper. You will see a ghostly area of **green**.

TRADITIONAL COLOUR WHEEL

PRIMARY	SECONDARY	TERTIARY	COMPLEMENTARY
red	*orange*	*red-orange, orange-yellow*	*green*
yellow	*green*	*yellow-green, blue-green*	*violet*
blue	*violet*	*violet-blue, violet-red*	*orange*

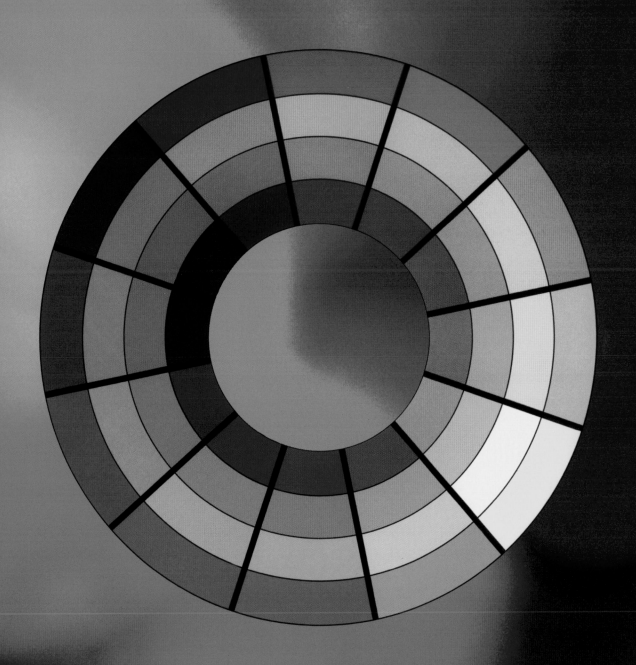

your colours

Each of us has a particular colouring – a natural 'colour scheme' consisting of the colours of our eyes, skin and hair. These colours may be inherited from our parents or – having skipped a generation, thanks to a non-dominant or 'recessive' gene – from one of our grandparents. Other factors can also play a part. If you are raised in a Mediterranean climate, for example, your residual skin colouring will grow darker and your hair may bleach from prolonged exposure to sunlight. Illness, too, can affect your complexion and hair colour. My grandmother went grey overnight as a result of a serious illness when still a young woman in the 1920s.

But our attractions to particular colours go far beyond a conscious decision to be in harmony with our hair or skin colouring. We are drawn to colours on an instinctive level, perhaps because they express something powerful and non-verbal about our personality and approach to life.

COLOUR'S HELP IN TIME OF NEED

In addition to having a permanent preference for a colour scheme, we may feel drawn to particular colours at times of exhaustion, stress or emotional need. We need the boost of a particular colour vibration to correct our body's balance of energies. At the simplest level, we all feel the effect of putting on bright party clothes – perhaps in vivid red, lordly purple or glittering silver or gold – which enliven us even if we are tired or lethargic. If you are working at home for a day and can

GET TO KNOW YOURSELF BETTER

If you have a strong preference for a particular colour, you are likely to have the characteristics associated with that colour.

- **red** – extrovert, excitable, sensuous, passionate, full of energy

- **orange** – independent-minded, strong-willed, a self-starter

- **green** – sensitive, observant, diplomatic, caring and careful

- **yellow** – capable, quick-witted, spontaneous, confident, a good communicator

- **blue** – creative, imaginative, deep-feeling, sincere

- **purple** – compassionate, intuitive, with high standards

- **white** – broadminded, a perfectionist, optimistic, self-sufficient

- **black** – self-disciplined, full of opinions, independent, possessing inner strength

choose where to settle down, you may find yourself choosing one room over another because of the interaction between its colour scheme and your mood. If you have to cope with a bereavement or shock, you may seek solace in green, the soothing colour of the heart, perhaps by going for country walks or wearing a comfortable green mackintosh or scarf. At this and similar times you are drawn to the vibrational energy of one colour above others.

Equally, you may have a strong reaction against a colour, indicating that you are overloaded with that colour's vibration – you will benefit from incorporating its complementary colour into your life (see pages 14–15). For example, if you feel a strong negative response to orange at a particular time, find something blue to look at or wear – or buy a blue hanging to put in your home. Develop your sensitivity to your body's responses to colour and follow your instincts.

YOUR NATURAL COLOURS

Our natural colouring usually has a powerful influence on the colours we prefer to wear.

- people with **fair** or **blond** hair, who usually have **green**, **blue** or **grey** eyes, are generally attracted by the colours **green** or **blue**

- people with **brown** eyes and dark hair/complexion often choose rich, bright colours

- **red-headed** people are another group who tend to like **blues** and **greens**

changing colours

We all have a vital and subtle connection to colour in the world around us, seeing colours differently as the quality of light changes at various times of the day and night. On a day of rest or illness, you may have watched the effects of changing daylight on the wall of your room – and perhaps noticed how at different times the colours in your curtains or rug appear to vary under the influence of a light in which different colours predominate.

Imagine being a silent witness for a 24-hour span in a summer garden. Think of the pale, bluish light just before sunrise and the warmer, yellowish colours of afternoon sunlight. Consider the purple-violet shadows and milky whiteness of the scene bathed peacefully in moonlight.

PRESIDING COLOURS

Being attuned to the presiding or ruling colour at a particular time of day can help us to feel a deeper personal harmony and a more intimate integration with the outside world. In the dawn light, blue is predominant. As the morning progresses, blue shades through turquoise into darker greens. Around the middle of the day, the green light begins to turn yellow. Throughout the afternoon, yellow darkens, becoming a rich reddish-orange by early evening. As the evening progresses, orange light becomes red and then turns to mauve. Mauve shifts into magenta and in the midnight hours magenta becomes a rich purple. About halfway between midnight and dawn, purple is overtaken by violet.

Those of us living in northern latitudes are affected by these different light vibrations even in the winter months, when we spend a great deal of time in darkness.

SEASONAL COLOURS

A parallel cycle of colour change can be traced through the seasons. Winter, spring, summer, autumn – each has its own unmistakable energy flow and collection of colours.

A winter landscape is often one of stark contrasts – a bare black tree silhouetted against a pale sky, or a dark-looking, twiggy hedge dissecting a snow-covered field. Bright berries or dark evergreen leaves stand out all the more clearly against frosty ground or the chilly white-grey of winter clouds.

In spring, green shoots rise and the whites, pastel pinks and blues of blossoms delight the eye. We look out for banks of yellow daffodils.

Summer suggests the golden yellows of sunshine and crops, the pale blues of the cloudless sky and the sea that restlessly reflects it, with lavender and the pinks of flowers.

In autumn, rich colours come to the fore – the russet brown, gold, earthy red and orange of falling leaves and the mellow, burnished crops that are carried in from the fields.

SEASONAL PERSONALITIES

The colour theorist Johannes Itten, an artist who worked at the Bauhaus school of design, architecture and arts in Germany, developed the theory that people fall into one of four seasonal types depending on whether their natural colouring belongs to winter, spring, summer or autumn. Itten noticed that his art students were attracted to colours that were attuned to their seasonal type. Later theorists developed and elaborated these observations, identifying particular traits of character that could be associated with different seasonal types.

WHAT SEASONAL TYPE ARE YOU?

Colour theorists suggest that each of the different seasonal types has typical associated personality traits.

- **winter type** Dark brown or black hair; brown, black or green eyes; brown, olive or beige complexion. Winter personalities are responsible and self-possessed, with natural authority and a will to get things done; you may need to fight an impulse to be impatient with others and be careful not to dismiss efforts that fall short of your standards.

- **spring type** Golden-brown or blond hair; hazel, green or blue-grey eyes; a light, peach-coloured complexion. Spring personalities are extrovert, charming and caring, with a lively sense of fun. They may take on too much at once and risk becoming disorganized.

- **summer type** Light brown or light blond hair; grey-brown, grey or pale misty blue eyes; a smooth, light complexion. If you are a summer personality, you are a gentle soul and a sensitive listener who is strong on cooperation, analysis and organization. Good at making and keeping the peace, you may sometimes appear withdrawn or aloof.

- **autumn type** Red, copper or strawberry-blond hair; brown or green eyes; a copper or dark golden complexion. Autumn personalities are warm and lively, and strong thinkers with a well-developed sense of justice and a healthy disregard for convention. They can be moody and may sometimes be accused of being bossy.

colours in nature

Colour plays a vital role in the natural world. Plants and animals depend on the cycles and colours of natural light to regulate their growth and behaviour from day to day and season to season. Creatures are guided in their movements and appetites by the passage from the purple-violet hours of night to the blue light of dawn, and the ensuing changes in the predominant colours of light during the day (see page 18). As autumn draws to a close, the shortening hours of daylight prepare the plant and animal kingdoms for the winter regime, while the combination of colours in the longer days after winter's end make possible the regeneration of spring.

ANIMAL COLOURS

Colour also serves as a vibrant language in the animal kingdom. The wasp wears its distinctive yellow-and-black-striped colouring as a warning to predators and other creatures to stay away. Red or yellow/black is often a signal of danger among fish, insects and plants. Brilliant colours in fish or bird plumage are used to differentiate the sexes and attract a mate. But these colours may appear different to various species.

NIGHT HUNTERS

Cats, owls, foxes and other night-time hunters have highly developed night vision. They can see longer wavelengths of light than humans, including the infrared waves we experience as heat. Being able to 'see' heat helps a cat track hidden prey – and this ability also explains why cats always find the warmest place in the home. But cats have less developed vision in the field of colours seen by humans. They see blue and green and a little red, but not very clearly.

UNDERWATER SONG

Apart from apes, the majority of mammals have less developed colour vision than humans. But they have enhanced sensitivity in other regions of the electromagnetic spectrum – for example, many have very acute hearing. Male humpback whales communicate by singing songs at very low frequencies that travel great distances underwater. These songs, believed to be part of the mating ritual, can last for 30 minutes each.

DO BULLS SEE RED?

Scientists know that a bull sees essentially in **black**, **white** and **grey** — but the bull nevertheless responds to colour vibrations, just as blind people are aware of different colours without seeing them. Therefore, the bull may appear to be enraged by a **red** rag even though it does not see it as 'red'.

LIGHT AND NAVIGATION

A clear sky contains a well-ordered pattern of polarized light. Humans cannot see it, but – according to latest scientific thinking – birds, fish and even dung beetles use it for navigation. Polarized light is light that vibrates in a single plane, whereas normal light rays have random, multi-directional vibrations.

A NEW COLOUR DIMENSION

Most birds, bees and other animals experience colour quite differently from humans. Bees and many other insects, for example, are sensitive to ultraviolet light, the short-wavelength colours that are beyond the range of the human eye. Scientists suspect that bees can see ultraviolet guidelines that lead them to pollen in flowers.

In humans, colour sensations are generated when light stimulates a combination of three types of cone in the eye (see page 12). But some creatures – including birds, some fish and turtles – have four types of cone, enabling them to see a wider range of colours and also giving them a different experience of the colours visible to humans. Since this is beyond our experience, we can only imagine what the colours of this new dimension must look like.

Birds, too, can see ultraviolet light. Scientists have found that certain seeds, flowers and fruits stand out from background vegetation much more clearly in ultraviolet wavelengths than in human-wavelength colours. Humans appreciate the variety of brilliant colours in bird plumage. The birds themselves may see far more than us – tiny differences that we miss, for example in the feathers of male and female blue tits, are much more clearly visible at ultraviolet wavelengths.

ways with colour

Colours have deep-seated symbolic associations that feed into our responses to clothes, plants, decorative schemes and the play of light. Some of these colour meanings cross the boundaries of language and culture, representing a shared bank of memories that go back to our distant ancestors; others appear to be specific to certain locations and cultures.

Red, the colour of blood, symbolizes life itself. In many places, red suggests the earth and the sun at sunrise and sunset. It also has connotations of accessible sexuality – prostitutes have traditionally advertised their services with a red light and were sometimes called 'scarlet women'. The colour's associations with spilt blood mean that red is also sometimes suggestive of violence and warfare. In Ghana, red is a colour of death – mourners wear red to honour the memory of a dead relative.

In Western cultures, white has well-established associations with purity and virginity, as seen in the bridal dress and veil. The colour suggests the milky light of the moon, and derives some of its virginal associations from its connection to Artemis, a Greek moon goddess who was a fierce defender of sexual purity.

COLOURS OF THE HEAVENS

The sun, moon and each of the planets is traditionally associated with a different colour and a distinctive quality or influence.

PLANET/BODY	COLOUR	PLANET'S ASSOCIATIONS
Sun	yellow	linked to Apollo, Greek god of music and poetry
Moon	white	promotes chastity
Mars	red	brings war
Jupiter	blue	brings happiness
Venus	green	presides over love
Mercury	purple	the Roman god Mercury was a messenger and god of trade
Saturn	black	associated with time, and in the astrological tradition an evil planet to be born under

In China, however, white is linked with death and is the colour of the mourning shroud. A bride who wore a white dress would be bringing unhappiness upon herself; instead she wears red, the Chinese colour of happiness. In many cultures, white is held to be a sacred colour (see page 24).

Blue is linked with the sky and water. The Roman sky god Jupiter and his goddess–spouse Juno were associated with blue. It is said to be the colour of love, and a bride traditionally carries a blue item on her wedding day. Blue is also linked to sincerity, religious faith, hopefulness and a clear conscience.

Green is associated with healing, balance and the natural world. In the folk tradition of central and northern Europe, the Green Man personifies nature's creative powers. He appears in art and as an architectural feature, often with a face made of foliage or with leaves and shoots coming out of his mouth, ears and eyes.

Yellow, the colour of fallen leaves, has autumnal connections. In Egypt it was traditionally the colour of mourning; at one time, widows in the Brittany region of France wore yellow caps as a sign that they had been touched by death. It also has associations with cowardice and betrayal; in France, national traitors had their doors daubed with yellow paint as a mark of shame. In the Christian tradition, Judas Iscariot, the betrayer of Christ, is usually depicted in yellow robes. Yellow is also linked with sickness – yellowing skin can be a sign of illness, and yellow was traditionally used to mark an area of quarantine.

But rich yellows may be connected with sunlight, joyful vitality and strength. Christ's disciple Peter is often shown in rich yellow robes. In ancient China, yellow was the imperial colour, and the doorway to the emperor's palace was called the 'yellow door'.

Traditionally associated with power and a prominent position in society, purple was a favourite colour of the Egyptian queen Cleopatra. It was also the colour worn by Roman emperors. Before synthetic purple dye was developed in the 19th century, natural purple dye was very expensive. In ancient times, 'royal' or 'imperial' purple was laboriously made from the shells of molluscs. Purple is also linked with intuition and imagination – according to colour theorists, purple bedroom walls will boost a child's imaginative powers.

Black is the colour of the grave, of death and of mourning in the Western tradition, and is linked with evil, magic and the 'dark arts'. However, black and grey are also the colours traditionally favoured by priests, and black is the colour of sophisticated formal wear. In ancient Egypt, black was the colour of the goddess Isis, and black cats were seen as sacred to the goddess and possessed of divine powers.

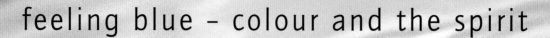

feeling blue – colour and the spirit

Colour has tremendous spiritual force. Its energy can stimulate and uplift the soul, while its symbolic meanings enrich religious expression. The powerful associations and inspirational qualities of colour inform the world's great religious traditions.

White has been associated with holiness since at least the era of the Persian Zoroastrian religion in the 6th century BC. In the Judaeo-Christian tradition, white is the colour of angels' wings and of the robes worn by Christ after his resurrection. It is also associated with peace – and is the colour of the dove chosen by Christians as the image of the Holy Spirit.

Darker shades of blue were the colours of the Mother and Earth Goddess worshipped by ancient pagans; in the Christian tradition, blue was the colour linked to the Virgin Mary, mother of Christ, who was taken into the heavens at the Assumption. Christians traditionally hold that a blue cloth draped over a coffin symbolizes immortality. Sky blue has general connotations of spiritual awareness, understanding and depth of character and is particularly associated with Hindu gods – especially Krishna, one of the incarnations of the god Vishnu. Krishna is represented with light blue skin, which indicates to Hindus that he has the power to overcome evil.

Green is sacred in Islam and was said to be the colour of the prophet Muhammad's robe. In Christian imagery, green represents the resurrection of the dead, while pale green is linked with the rite of baptism, in which new church members are blessed with holy water. In both Islam and Christianity, red is associated with the blood of those who sacrificed themselves in the cause of their religion. In India, yellow is often the colour of renunciation of worldly appetites – in the Buddhist tradition, monks wear yellow or orange robes – but in the Hindu festival of Holi, bright yellow, red and other colours are used to celebrate the arrival of spring.

Purple, associated with royalty and secular power, is also a colour of intuition and spiritual power. It is the colour of bishops' robes in the Christian church, reflecting both their pre-eminence and spiritual authority. It also has connections with grief and sadness over wrongdoing: some Christian churches are decorated with purple on Ash Wednesday, at the start of Lent; purple also appears on the Saturday of Easter week, the day following Good Friday.

Some religious groups associate grey, black or brown with a life of moderation, simplicity and love of others. These colours are chosen by many Christian monastic groups for their robes. Early Quakers chose to wear grey, brown or black as a sign that they had rejected frippery and chosen a simple life.

COLOUR AND MOOD

Which colours represent various moods? The connection between colour and mood is well established in everyday language.

- **blue** – associated with the phrases 'feeling blue' and 'got the blues', which mean feeling depressed, battered by events, but perhaps with a steely resilience; blues music can give someone an energetic spiritual uplift through keen feeling and expression of sadness

- **green** – associated with the phrases 'green-eyed monster' or 'green with envy', meaning jealous or envious

- **yellow** – associated with the phrase 'yellow-bellied', meaning cowardly

- **red** – associated with the phrase 'seeing red', which means getting angry or ready for violence in a flash

- **black** – associated with the phrase 'a black mood', which means unable to see a way forward or to feel any hope

colour and the senses

A scent can lift or depress our whole mood; it can disgust us physically or transport our imagination to a place of brightly coloured memories. Our sense of smell and our sense of taste are so closely linked that we can sometimes taste a bad odour. There may also be a mental connection between the senses of smell and sight. Most of us make subconscious associations between odours and colours and tend to prefer scents that are in harmony with the vibrations of the colours we like.

COLOUR AND EVAPORATION IN PERFUMES

Perfume-makers describe the oils they mix in their scents – according to how quickly or slowly the oils evaporate – as 'top notes', 'middle notes' and 'base notes'. Top notes are those that evaporate fastest; bottom notes are those that evaporate most slowly. The best perfumes usually contain a blend of top notes, middle notes and base notes. The range of 'notes' in oils can be overlaid on the spectrum of rainbow colours. Base notes have deeper vibrations and align with the longer waves of the red end of the spectrum, while top notes have lighter vibrations and are equivalent to the violet end of the rainbow.

PLEASANT AND UNPLEASANT

We are attracted by the smell of plants and materials that have bright or clear colours – **orange**, **lemon**, **violet**, **pine** and **roses**.

We try to avoid the smells of **brown**, **grey** and **black** substances.

The odours of **green**, **lavender**, **pale yellow** and **pink** plants tend to be the most attractive.

Foods such as fish or vinegar, which often come in dull or cloudy colours, have unpleasant smells.

COLOUR AND AROMATHERAPY

Aromatherapists who use natural scented oils in healing teach that some scents harmonize with a person's colour vibrations while others do not. In particular they will often ask a client which of the rainbow colours she is particularly drawn to at times of crisis or illness, since this may indicate a deficiency in the chakra or energy centre associated with that colour. (The body's chakras are described on pages 112–14.)

SYNAESTHESIA

People with the medical condition synaesthesia 'see' scents or tastes as colours. Medical experts believe that the condition arises when genetic abnormalities cause unusual connections to form between the parts of the brain that receive signals about scent, taste and colour, causing the functions to become entangled. Many of us may imagine a colour when we encounter a scent, but people with synaesthesia actually have the sensation of seeing the colours.

There are several types of synaesthesia. Some people with the condition experience sounds as colours, while other people see different colours for each letter and word. Artists in many fields have or have had synaesthesia. They include the writer Vladimir Nabokov, the artists Wassily Kandinsky and David Hockney, and the composers Franz Liszt and Olivier Messiaen.

ARE YOUR FAVOURITE COLOURS CONNECTED WITH YOUR FAVOURITE SCENTS?

Test the theory that colour preferences are closely tied to choice of perfume by comparing your own likes and dislikes against this checklist.

- if your preferred colours are **green** and **rustic brown**, your favourite scents may be **citrus** or **earthy**

- if you prefer **silvery greys** and **pastel colours**, your favourite scents may be **flowers** and **non-citrus fruits**

- if your preferred colours are **deep green** and **orange**, your favourite scents may be **woody**

- if you prefer **terracotta** and **red-purple**, your favourite scents may be **heavily spiced** and **autumnal**

- if your preferred colours are **white**, **black** and **cream**, your favourite scents may be **leather** and **incense**

colour and clothes

unspoken language

Each day, the clothes you wear send out messages about who you are and the kind of person you aspire to be. You may have a favourite 'look' – formal, sporty, country, urban, futuristic or bohemian – and you probably also adapt your outfit to fit in with your natural skin and hair colouring and your colour preferences. The colour scheme affects both you yourself and the people around you – the personality your chosen colours represent is a central part of the first impression that you create, whether you are meeting friends, colleagues, family members, acquaintances or strangers.

COLLECTIVE CONSCIOUSNESS

The zeitgeist, or 'spirit of the age', is reflected in colour fashions as well as in political and religious attitudes and artistic tastes. Changing fashions in colour may reflect our shared psychological needs. For example, the early years of the 21st century have seen an enthusiasm for blue, a calming colour believed to boost good communication – perhaps reflecting our unspoken shared understanding that we need to turn away from conflict and talk peace. The popularity of 'natural' colours such as leaf green and terracotta reflects widespread concern about environmental issues.

Some major companies – from car manufacturers to interior designers – invest large sums of money in researching which colours and colour combinations will become fashionable. The taste for blue will, they say, be followed by one for orange – an optimistic colour of health, sociability and the fulfilment of potential.

WHAT THE COLOURS OF YOUR CLOTHES SAY ABOUT YOU

If you are going to a job interview, for example, or meeting someone for the first time, study the information below to see how the colour of your clothes can help you to project the image you desire.

- **blue** Sky blue suggests that you have a sincere, sensitive, trustworthy and creative personality; darker blue suggests that you are intelligent, responsible and decisive.

- **orange** You seem extrovert, energetic, adventurous and full of ideas. You signal that you can be relied upon to take action and get results.

- **red** You are passionate and brave, a good leader with high standards. In some contexts, red worn by women may carry a sensual or erotic charge.

- **yellow** You exude confidence and happiness, suggesting that you are intelligent, clear-thinking and able to cope with challenges. You are resourceful and positive in outlook.

- **indigo** Indigo or violet projects a compassionate nature. You love knowledge and peace, and find satisfaction in helping others.

- **pink** You have confidence in yourself and are at peace with your feminine, intuitive side.

- **brown** Down-to-earth and reliable, you enjoy the good life – food, drink and conviviality. You can be relied on to avoid flights of fancy.

- **green** Calm and diplomatic, you are good at finding peaceful solutions. You have an open, observant mind and no fear of change – although you are cautious when necessary.

- **purple** You seem to be a spiritual and intuitive person who shows great sensitivity.

- **white** You seek perfection. You carry joy in your heart, and are optimistic about the way forward. You follow your own path and are not dependent on the approval of others.

- **black** Authoritative, strong-willed and well organized, you give the impression of inner strength. You are efficient and self-controlled, probably a good leader. Wearing black and grey – the colours of monks and priests – may suggest that you prefer a simple life.

GOOD AND BAD

All colours have both positive and negative associations. Generally, clear and bright shades of a colour have a positive, pleasing effect, while its dark, cloudy shades evoke a more negative response.

vibrational harmonies

Few of us dress in a single colour, choosing instead to team a dominant colour with secondary colours whose vibrational energy harmonizes both with our state of mind and with the main colour. Sometimes we choose a colour designed to boost our sense of wellbeing or project a particular image, but then undermine the effect by mixing it with a disruptive colour. Equally, in some colour mixes, the secondary colour reinforces the effect of the main one to make us feel calmer, more focused or more impassioned. The effect of your colour mix is enhanced when you use a dark shade of one colour with a light tint of the other. A rust-red jacket or cardigan offsets a cream shirt or blouse, and suggests that you are adventurous and enthusiastic but also have a balancing strain of perfectionism; your dark grey suit looks elegant when matched with a pale pink blouse or shirt, and projects an impression of competence and self-confidence with a touch of intuition.

A FULL-SPECTRUM OUTFIT

If your spirits and vitality levels are high, you can mix colours as you please. In this state of mind, you will not suffer negative effects from combinations whose vibrational energy might upset you when you are feeling low. For pure enjoyment and self-expression, you could try mixing all the colours of the rainbow in your outfit – but make sure you keep some of them inconspicuous. You might want to wear a red T-shirt with sky-blue jeans and green socks, for example, but confine other strong colours to underwear, jewellery and accessories.

COMBINING COLOURS IN AN OUTFIT

*When deciding which colours to combine for a positive effect,
consult the colour wheel on page 15.*

- **complementary colours** Hues on opposite sides of the wheel go together well; their energies balance and boost one another. Orange and dark blue or yellow and violet, for example, make striking, vibrant contrasts.

- **bicomplementary colours** Mixing a colour with the colour alongside the complementary on the colour wheel (its bicomplementary) is another good recipe. For example, if you mix orange with blue-green, the outfit will have a positive impact. If you want to replace the violet trousers you wore with your yellow shirt, a blue-violet pair will do as well.

- **harmonious colours** Neighbouring colours often combine well. If you mix tones of the same colour or of neighbouring colours, the contrast will boost the enlivening or calming effect of that range of the spectrum. If you wear trousers in navy blue with a sky blue shirt and a royal-blue tie or brooch, you will be calmed and project an image of creativity tempered by responsibility.

COLOURS AND COMPLEXION

Keep your natural colouring in mind when choosing clothes. **Greens** tend to be a safe bet for everyone.

If you have dark hair and a dark complexion, your recommended colours are **white**, **bronze** or **gold**, **turquoise**, **dark or pale blue**, **green**

If you have dark hair and a light complexion, your colours are **black**, **white**, **dark blue**, **turquoise**, **green**

If you have fair hair and high skin colour, your colours are **rose**, **pink**, **blue-purple**, **aquamarine**, **green**

If you have fair hair and pale skin, your colours are **brown**, **golden yellow**, **blue** and **green**, **maroon**

If you have red hair, your colours are **dark brown**, **deep blue**, **green**, **orange**, **terracotta**

workaday colours

For some of us, one of the worst aspects of Monday morning is putting away the bright, expressive clothes of the weekend and clambering back into a work outfit. But we all have plenty of opportunities to express ourselves with colour, even in the context of our working lives.

COLOUR AT WORK

If you have to wear a uniform at work, you usually won't have to put it on until you clock in, so why not select an outfit in mood-enhancing colours to wear on the way to and from work? Choose your accessories with care – even during the day you will absorb the colour vibrations of your underwear or the T-shirt or other clothing you wear under a uniform.

If you feel a strong attraction to particular colours, carry coloured cloths or cards with you. You can either display them around your work area or, if there is somewhere where you can relax in private, use them to soothe your spirits or boost your energy levels during your break. If allowed, wear a brooch or ring – or carry a gemstone – in one of your preferred colours.

ACCESSORY COLOURS

If you have to wear a dark business suit and sensible shoes to work, you can still express your personality through the colours of the accessories you choose.

- **red** – energetic, has leadership qualities

- **orange** – confident

- **blue** – creative, trustworthy

- **green** – calm, diplomatic

- **yellow** – intellectual, with good reasoning skills

- **indigo** – good team player, easy to work with

- **violet** – understanding, knowledgeable

- **purple** – intuitive

- **pink** – sensitive, confident, flamboyant

DRESSING FOR THE JOB

Some colours are particularly well suited to certain occupations, while others should be avoided. For example, if you are a businessperson or banker, black, grey or dark blue will project authority and reliability. A red tie or other accessory suggests that you are energetic and unstinting in pursuing your clients' goals; accessories in violet or indigo indicate that you are purposeful and capable of inspired thinking.

EMPHASIZING YOUR ROLE

If you are a teacher, a health practitioner or a complementary healer, wearing blue suggests that you are knowledgeable and dedicated to serving others; light blue suggests a creative capacity for healing. Add orange accents to signal that you have mental energy and independence, or yellow to signal a powerful intellect. If you have to give lectures, be sure to wear bright colours, which will help to make your performance at the lectern eye-catching and memorable. Avoid all-white or all-black outfits.

A lawyer or public servant might wear dark blue or green with a red tie or brooch: the blue suggests dedicated service, and the green an optimistic outlook; red indicates energy and a passionate pursuit of the goal tempered by the more sober blues and greens of the main suit.

Architects, writers, musicians, artists and designers are free to combine colours to reflect their own preferences and colour vibrations. A mixture of bright colours will tend to stimulate creativity while suggesting to potential clients and others that they are fresh-thinking, perhaps unconventional, with an open mind.

If you are pregnant, on maternity leave, a full-time mother or a nursery teacher, wearing green and light blue or pastel shades is soothing for the body and for your young charges.

CORPORATE COLOURS

Some corporations ask staff to wear uniforms to project an image. What are the subliminal meanings of uniforms worn by staff in courier firms, restaurant chains or local street-cleaning and refuse-collection teams?

- **orange** – polite and happy, friendly when interacting with the public, lively

- **blue** – reliable, calm in an emergency

- **green** – approachable, cooperative outlook, capable at outdoor work such as tending parks or gardens

- **brown** – helpful, solid and secure, not self-important

- **red** – quick in response, will find solution to problems

- **yellow** – good at understanding and communicating ideas

BLUE: THE COLOUR OF SERVICE

In imperial China during the Han dynasty (206BC–AD220), officials and lords wore coloured silk ribbons at court as a mark of status. Aristocrats and military leaders wore **purple**; royals wore **red** and officials wore **blue**. In ancient Rome, too, **blue** was the colour worn by public servants.

time to unwind

Many people returning home after a day's work like to change from their business clothes into looser fitting, perhaps less sombre outfits. If you are one of those, pick colours that will help you to relax. If you are feeling stressed after work and want to flop and do nothing at home, choose green, blue or pastel tints that will encourage you to unwind. Your best bet is to stay natural – you will probably find it easiest to relax if you avoid garments containing artificial colours and fibres.

If you want to unwind totally, choose pyjamas or nightgowns in comfortable dark shades of blue and green, perhaps even mauve or purple, rather than bright or busy designs. These will ease your spirits towards restful slumber.

CELEBRATION COLOURS

When you are psychologically drained and feeling in need of a lift – say, on a dark winter's evening after trailing home through the rain – energizing colours such as orange or red may help to revitalize you. If you are spending only a short time at home before going out for the evening, change into something bright and cheerful.

Think of the style of clothes you might wear on holiday in a warm place. They will probably be in simple bright colours or complex patterns. Many people find that bringing out these 'celebration colours' helps to lift the spirits – not least by recalling the long sunlit days of summer at times when your body is feeling the lack of natural light.

RESISTING FASHION

Whether you are staying in or going out, try to resist being browbeaten by fashion – hard as that may be when there is nothing but khaki in the shops. You will feel your best when you wear the colour scheme that expresses your personality and is attuned to your natural colouring. Don't force yourself into turquoise or silver because it is the colour of the moment. If you do, it may make you feel ill at ease because the vibrational energy of the colours you are wearing is at odds with your own energy.

HOW GOOD IS YOUR RELATIONSHIP?

The colours that we choose to wear and surround ourselves with in our own living spaces are eloquent expressions of our personality type. If we are attracted to single colours at particular times – perhaps when we are overworked, depressed or grieving – this preference reveals a great deal about our state of mind and current aspirations.

Have you thought about whether your natural colouring and colour preferences complement those of your partner? Do you find yourself approving of his or her colour choices? Or do you wish he or she would take your advice on this matter?

Consider your partner's colour choices in clothes, shoes, house furnishings and decoration – even food. It bodes well for the long-term health of your relationship if your colour preferences blend harmoniously.

THE POWER OF GEMS AND CRYSTALS

The tradition of using gemstones and crystals for healing and spiritual strength stretches back at least to the culture of ancient Egypt. Natural stones and crystals embody the power and associations of their colour.

Turquoise crystals are highly valued for their protective and healing properties; **blue** stones promote creativity; **yellow** stones will help you to think clearly; **red** ones are energizing and may be useful in stimulating blood flow; **green** crystals and stones can heal and soothe a troubled spirit; **white** and sparkling stones can recharge your energy and boost your confidence.

Wear crystals and stones in rings, pendants, bracelets or brooches. Place them around your home or office to heal your spirits and protect against electromagnetic and spiritual pollution.

the young ones

Colours make a strong impression on children from infancy. The play of light and colour speaks directly to the spirit and has deep meaning for babies even before they can use words. Toddlers and children will have positive associations for years with a colour that they link to a good experience – perhaps the pastel shade of the room where their mother or father lovingly cradled them or the colour of their comfort blanket, if they had one. Equally, a colour associated with a childhood trauma can make individuals feel uncomfortable or distressed many years afterwards.

BABIES

Young babies are constantly adjusting to their surroundings. All is fresh and new, and they are faced with a barrage of sensory stimuli every waking hour. Pastel blues and pinks were the traditional colours for babies' clothes, but the modern fashion in Western society is for bright colour combinations and vibrant patterns. There is a view that we should be wary of overstimulation; if you want to protect your baby's sensitivity, you can dress her or him in soft and pale colours with a gentle vibrational energy, such as pale blue, pink, gently earthy greens, cream and rock greys.

OLDER CHILDREN

Toddlers and older children often favour brighter reds, blacks, blues and oranges in dynamic patterns. Encourage them to express themselves through colour. They will spend plenty of time at nursery and primary school with water-based paints and with crayons in many colours and proudly bring their artwork home. Discuss their colour choices with them. Try to get a sense of the colours that speak strongly to them. Use colour generously in the home – perhaps by introducing lampshades, rugs and cushions in the colours of the spectrum in your children's rooms or allowing them to have brightly coloured clothes and accessories such as trainers, hats and toys.

EARLY TEENS

From around the age of ten into the early teens, children tend to become much more conscious of prevailing fashion and nervous of provoking disapproval at school if they go against what everyone else is wearing. At this age, fashion may largely dictate their colour preferences in public, but try to encourage them to keep in mind the colours that speak to them privately and deeply. Help them to keep a place for those colours as long as they retain their significance – perhaps in the choice of pyjamas, dressing gown, slippers or casual 'home' clothes.

CHILDHOOD PROBLEMS: COLOURFUL SOLUTIONS

Careful use of colour can reinforce the effect of medical treatments if your child has physical or behavioural problems.

- **hyperactive?** He or she may be calmed by wearing **blue**, **green** or **yellow**, especially in light tones.

- **skin rash?** Try earthy **brown** or **green** in natural fabrics.

- **can't sleep?** Wear **turquoise**, **blue** or **white** pyjamas and use bed linen in these colours.

- **asthma?** Wearing **blue** or **white** may help to relax muscles and ease symptoms; do not dress your child in **red** or **black** because they often have the opposite effect.

- **listless and inactive?** Try dressing your child in energizing **orange** or **red**.

HEALING COLOURS

Colour therapists find that children under the age of eight have a particular attraction to and affinity with **blue**, representing peace, and **orange**, the colour of joy. In those who have the gift of healing, this colour affinity lasts into adulthood.

protecting yourself

We can use the colour energy of clothes not only to raise our spirits or give ourselves a lift when we are at a low ebb, but also to protect our bodies and minds against illnesses or negative states of mind.

A red shirt appears red because its fabric absorbs all rays of the spectrum except red. When an individual wears a red shirt, the energizing red vibration passes through the shirt and bathes the body – as well as bouncing off the shirt to make an impression on other people.

When someone wears white, the outfit absorbs none of the vibrations of light, so that the full spectrum of colour

DOES THE COLOUR OF YOUR CLOTHES MAKE YOU UNCOMFORTABLE?

We have all worn clothes that are the right size and cut in a soft natural material but don't feel right. We may be hard pressed to explain precisely why we don't like the shirt or jumper we ignore — but the reason is likely to be that we feel uncomfortable with any colour that is subtly discordant with our natural colouring or our colour preferences.

COLOUR COMBINING FOR HEALTH

When choosing colours to boost mental or physical wellbeing, take care which secondary colours you combine with them – some colours will change the effect of the first-choice colour. White is generally a safe choice and can be worn with any other colour.

- if your first-choice colour is **purple**, team it with **blue** or **white**

- if your first-choice colour is **blue**, a health-promoting partner is **white** or, sometimes, **turquoise**

- if your first-choice colour is **green**, **turquoise** is a good secondary

- if your first-choice colour is **magenta**, pair it with **white**; avoid **violet** or **red**

- if your first-choice colour is **violet**, choose **white**; avoid **blue** and **magenta**

- if your first-choice colour is **red**, team it with **yellow** or **white**

- if your first-choice colour is **orange**, make the secondary **yellow** or **white**; avoid **red**

- if your first-choice colour is **yellow**, combine it with **white**

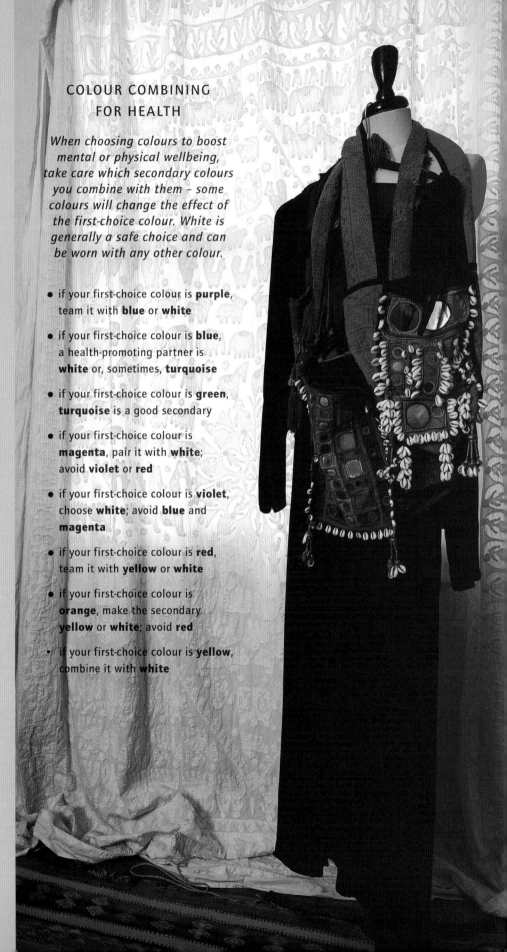

energy is available to that person; black absorbs all the colours, so a black outfit may provide a soothing 'shell' for someone feeling in need of protection. If we are attuned to our mental and physical needs, we can choose colours to protect against destructive patterns of thinking and to boost particular body systems.

DON'T WORK AGAINST YOURSELF

When you feel gloomy, picking out a bright colour or bright accessory for your business outfit may restore your spirits. But when you are feeling good, avoid wearing colours that work against your mood. If you awaken buzzing with optimism and full of energy, choose bright colours such as orange that reflect your state of mind. If you wear an all-grey or all-black outfit on a day of joy, you may end up feeling subtly discordant.

COLOURS AND CHAKRAS

According to the Hindu theory of the chakras (see pages 112–14), each of the body's seven chakras or energy centres is attuned to a colour and corresponds to a body system. For example, the throat chakra is attuned to blue and corresponds to the respiratory system – therefore, if you are prone to suffer from panic attacks accompanied by breathing difficulties, wearing soothing blue tones will be beneficial. The solar plexus, just below the navel, is attuned to yellow and corresponds to the digestive and nervous systems – therefore, yellow may help prevent indigestion. For a full list of the chakras and their associated colours and body systems, see page 114.

seasonal rhythms

We all experience the rhythms of nature – in the hours of light and darkness, in the changing seasons, in our fluctuating physical appetites and energy levels. We also have changing attitudes to, and affinities with, colour. In the long bright days of summer we tend to choose lighter colours such as pinks, sky blues, creams and whites; in the gloomy days of winter we are often drawn to darker shades of warming colours such as reds and oranges. We may find we dress in harmony with the seasons – bright blossom colours in spring, and leafy reds and greens in autumn. Equally, we might choose to go against seasonal effects, dispersing some of the dark of winter by donning the colours of summer or spring. If you keep track of the colours for which you feel a need, you will gain a deeper understanding of your biorhythms.

A COLOUR DIARY

Try keeping a record in a small book or folder of the colours that attract you at different times of the week and month, and through the changing seasons. You can collect swathes of material, postcards of paintings or views, paint-sample cards, clippings from magazines or even photocopies from home decorating books. If you are feeling artistic, record your colour impressions in wax crayon, pastels or watercolour. In autumn, gather and press some of the wonderfully coloured leaves found on a country walk, on a city pavement or in the park.

Your diary will help you to keep track of your colour moods and enthusiasms, as well as enabling you to align your colour

needs retrospectively with changes in physical health or spiritual buoyancy. Looking back, were you drawn to a particular colour at a time of illness or stress? When you felt joyful and fully confident of your capacity to rise to challenges, which colours were you in tune with?

Constituting your own personal compendium of colours, the diary will also prove a valuable resource if you are choosing colours for home decoration or for planting in the garden.

WHAT 'MISSING' COLOURS REVEAL ABOUT YOU

The colours that attract you in clothes and in other parts of your daily life may reflect a lack of the vibrational energy associated with those colours.

- **blue** If you notice a desire for blue, you are probably low on blue energy, which is associated with peace, decisiveness and intuition. To escape feelings of stress and distraction, make time to consider your options and do creative work.

- **red** An attraction to red may indicate lethargy, lack of energy and frustration with a drab routine. Perhaps you should change your exercise or sleep regime, or alter your diet to boost your vitality.

- **green** If you long for green, your spirit appears to be crying out for a soothing period of rest; try to take a step back from pressing circumstances in order to recuperate in natural surroundings and gain a fresh perspective.

- **indigo** or **violet** A longing for indigo or violet suggests that you are feeling cut off from your higher self. Consider taking a retreat or resuming a form of artistic self-expression – such as painting or music – that you may have abandoned. Look at the decisions you make every day. You are probably very busy – but how many of your activities are necessary? How many

could you give up with no loss to yourself or to others? Do you really have to sit in on that meeting? Do you get anything from watching that TV show? Indigo and violet energy will be abundant in your life when you have time to do things slowly, carefully and with full attention – when you have the peace occasionally to sit in silence and listen to your inner voice.

- **orange** A desire for orange suggests that you are feeling run down and in need of fresh impetus. Perhaps you have recently weathered a bad illness: you feel gloomy and trapped and are drawn to the colour of joy. Consider your leisure activities – do you have time for recreation? Try to reorganize your day to make space for yourself. Perhaps you need to look up an old friend who always cheers you up.

- **yellow** If you miss yellow, linked with happiness, self-confidence and wisdom, you may feel overwhelmed by challenges and in need either of support or of time to draw upon your own mental resources.

going natural

Clothes made from artificial fibres are usually cheaper to buy and easier to wash and handle than equivalent outfits made from natural fabrics. Modern manufacturers have developed an astonishing range of synthetic dyes – producing 'convenience clothes' in garish colours and flamboyant patterns. But, as we develop our awareness of colour and of our bodies' sensitivities, we frequently discover that we prefer the look and feel of natural fabrics and colourings. Unbleached and undyed cotton, for example, often sets off our natural skin-colouring better than a bleached bright-white material. The unbleached cloth comes in a range of subtle light browns and magnolia whites and creams that have a comfortable look. The material also feels softer to the skin – and, unlike bleached cloth, does not release traces of chemicals when washed.

Artificial fabrics do not sit easily on our bodies. Most football shirts and many running vests and shorts are made from lightweight, hard-wearing nylon that is very convenient but also interferes with our skin functions. When we wear nylon, our skin cannot breathe and the material generates static electricity that interferes with our bodily vibrations. Cotton shirts and sportswear may be more work to wash and dry, but they are far more comfortable to wear.

NATURAL TEXTURES

Texture is an important aspect of how clothes look. Different natural materials hold colour and absorb light in varying ways. Silk has a fine texture and holds rich colours; light playing on silk creates a delicate sheen that suggests the material's luxurious softness. Coarser in texture, wool holds natural dyes very well and can be used for pullovers, coats and suits in a wonderful range of colours. Cotton is an ideal material for work clothes because it is hard-wearing but also lets the skin breathe.

NATURAL LOOKS

Beauty shines from within – in a bright smile, sparkling eyes, a healthy glow to the skin. We safeguard our natural good looks by taking care of ourselves – making sure our diet contains a balance of minerals and vitamins, drinking plenty of water, getting as much sleep as we need. We do not need make-up to look beautiful, but most of us share the ancient desire to add drama and contrast to our faces with colour, and sometimes use make-up for self-expression and fun. Equally, many of us sometimes feel the need to take 'emergency action' if we are looking particularly run down or unwell. Just as natural materials harmonize with our physical being better than synthetic fibres, so eye make-up and lipsticks that convincingly mimic the colours of flesh complement our looks better than conspicuously artificial products.

MATERIAL HIERARCHY

Some branches of esoteric theory teach that each human being has four energy bodies.

On the familiar, visible plane we have our physical body. Beyond that we have our life-force, the form of energy identified as *chi* in Chinese schools of thought. At the next level we have our individual soul, and beyond that the higher self or spirit through which in meditation or religious experience we can acquire the sure knowledge that all life is one in God.

Experts associate each of the four most common natural fabrics with one of these energy bodies: wool is attuned to the physical body, linen to the life-force, cotton to the individual soul and silk to the spirit. A piece of silk dyed in **purple**, **indigo** or **violet**, colours of intuition and the spirit, has an unusual power.

colour in your home

colourful interiors

We all want the colours we use in our homes to create a memorable impact, but assessing the right colours and colour combinations for each part of a living space can be a challenging task. For example, think of the last time you visited a flat or house for the first time. What stimulated your initial response? First impressions are crucial. If you devote time and effort to planning the decoration of the front door, the hallway and the rooms leading off it, you will be pleasurably ushered into your home each time you return – and your living space will have a positive effect on visitors.

COLOUR HARMONY

If you imagine the colours you combine in one area of your home as voices singing together in a band or choir, you will get a sense of the importance of harmony and of the total effect. To make a pleasant sound, the voices must not only be in tune with one another but must also blend in terms of volume, timbre and sound quality. And it helps if they are singing the same song.

Harmony is the overriding consideration. The choir may have voices that are beautifully balanced in terms of timbre and volume, but if they sing in different keys the performance will not be pleasing. Likewise, when decorating your home, you may carefully balance colours for lightness and saturation, but if they do not harmonize the effect will be jarring.

MAKING GOOD PAIRS

If you are in any doubt about how to combine colours, you can refer to the colour wheel (see page 15) to determine which colours will go well together and which colour combinations are likely to be appropriate in different rooms.

For example, you will achieve a bold and striking contrast if you combine complementary colours – those that are directly opposite each another on the colour wheel, or those one-third of the way around the wheel from one another. Such a pairing can often be tiring to live with, so, while it might be suitable for a children's room, it should probably be avoided in the principal living room.

ASPECTS OF COLOUR

*The impression we create in our homes depends
not only on our choice of colour but also on the colour's
temperature, saturation, lightness and 'movement'.*

- **temperature** Referring to a colour's 'feel', temperature reflects the contexts in which we find the colour in the natural world. For example, **orange-red** suggests fire and has a warming feel, while **blue** may make us think of water pools and has a cooling effect.

- **saturation** The darkness or paleness of a colour reflects its saturation. **Yellow**, for instance, can range from a dark banana hue to the palest lemon wash. Combining a colour with **white** creates a pale 'tint' – for example, a pale blue pastel; combining a colour with **black** creates a dark 'shade' – such as a brown created by mixing yellow and black.

- **lightness** The lightness of a colour reflects its proximity to **white** or **black**. Yellow appears lighter than blue because it is closer to white.

- **movement** The illusion of a colour approaching or retreating from the eye is called movement. 'Warmer' colours such as **red** appear to move towards the observer, making a room seem smaller, while 'cooler' colours such as **light blue** seem to move away from the observer, making the most of a room's size.

MAGNETIC AND ELECTRICAL COLOURS

Colour therapy adds a dimension to our understanding
of colour by referring to warm hues such as **red/orange**
as magnetic colours and cool ones such as **blue** and **violet** as
electrical colours. Magnetic colours are linked to the earth and
our physical being, while electrical colours are associated with
the sky and connect to our spiritual essence.

Blind people — whose lack of sight encourages them to develop
an enhanced sensitivity to the vibrations of the electromagnetic
spectrum — can often tell magnetic colours from electrical
colours by touch alone.

combining colours

One of the joys of using colour in the home is that you can afford to be adventurous. If you make a mistake and find that the colour mixture you have chosen is unsatisfactory, you can easily and relatively inexpensively redecorate part of the room. But, if you spend plenty of time planning, you are unlikely to go wrong. Don't play safe – the right combination, one that speaks to your soul, will be a source of peace or joy every day for as long as you stay alive to its influence.

DON'T RUSH

Test colour combinations before taking the plunge. Buy sample paint pots and paint small patches of wall. This will give you a good idea of how the colours will look in their setting.

If you don't want to paint onto the wall, you can approximate the effect by painting the samples onto sheets of paper and hanging them in the room, but this will not give you such a clear idea of how the colour combination will look on the texture of your wall.

Take your time. See how the colours appear at different times of the day, when the light falls in a particular way. Ideally, you should wait a few months to see if your feeling changes as the light shifts from one season to the next.

THE BIG PICTURE

Our perception of a colour is altered by the colours we see alongside and around it, so it is wise to consider the look of a whole room rather than just one corner at a time. There may be existing components of a decorative scheme that need to be worked around – a deep-red Afghan rug, say, or a work of art or large film poster that forms the centrepiece of a living-room wall. If you are in the mood for a complete makeover, you may decide to move the rug elsewhere or put away the work of art for a while, but otherwise you will need to ensure that your decorative scheme harmonizes with their colours.

PLAY OF LIGHT

When making decisions about colour, consider how the room you are painting will be lit. For example, does it receive warm sunlight or a cooler, northern daylight? If there is very little natural light, you may want to use a mixture of wall-mounted and freestanding light fixtures to provide illumination. You have a wide choice of types of bulb, producing different qualities of light.

You may want to use coloured lights in the room or to add colour to natural light by means of window hangings made from fabric or stained glass.

In some rooms, you may plan to use candlelight most evenings.

CHOOSING GUIDE COLOURS

Guide colours – those that form the basis of your colour scheme – can be chosen instinctively.

- Assemble a selection of paint manufacturers' colour cards, magazine or book reproductions, swathes of material and splashes of sample paint on paper. Try to make sure that your selection represents a wide range and includes all the main colours of the spectrum.

- Pin your samples to the wall and sit in front of them for a few minutes. Close your eyes briefly.

- Under your breath make the following pledge: 'I will find the colours that have meaning for me, that will uplift and guide me.'

- Open your eyes slightly and view the colours through narrowed lids. One or two colours will connect with you. Pick them at once without analytical thought.

- Base a scheme on those colours, trying different shades and tones.

you and yours

Unless you live alone, most of the rooms in your home will be used by more than one person. When planning to decorate such rooms, you should try to take everyone's colour preferences into account, but that doesn't mean settling for a bland compromise – with a little creativity, it is usually possible to come up with a mutually satisfactory colour mix.

Try repeating the guide-colour exercise (see page 50) with your flatmate, partner or children. It may turn out that your colour preferences blend harmoniously with those of other people – but, if not, some negotiation will be necessary.

In theory, there is nothing to stop you from having strikingly different colour schemes in different rooms to accommodate the guide colours identified by each individual – a passionate red in your room, say, with pink and purple in your daughter's bedroom.

But you also need to consider the effect of moving from one room to the next and, where it applies, the effect of being able to see into one room from another. If you can see into the kitchen from the morning room, say, you need to ensure that the colour schemes of the two rooms

do not clash. Even when you cannot see from one room to the next, you will probably want to avoid a jolting feeling when you move from one colour scheme to a second.

COLOUR IDEAS

If you are stumped for ideas, look around you. Colour inspiration is on every side. In spring, the delicate pink and white blossoms on the trees contrast with the deep maroon of a parked car; at the end of the street you glimpse a rainbow. In summer, you see a yellow sweep of cornfield against the blue sky. In autumn you take pleasure in the hues of root vegetables or the delicate complexity of reds and rusty browns in fallen leaves. Winter surprises you with a red burst of berries against evergreen or a splash of yellow sunlight suspended in misty air. Visit an art gallery or look at some home decorating books and magazines for further ideas. Recall your travels – think of the bright colours used in India, Mexico, South Africa. Sometimes you may want to plan a whole colour scheme around a treasured possession such as an antique vase or an inherited set of cups and saucers.

THE RIGHT COLOURS FOR THE ROOM

When planning a colour scheme, ask yourself the following questions.

How big is the room? Do I need to make it look bigger? (If so, choose cool rather than warm colours.) What is the room used for? Do I want a restful, zesty or illuminating atmosphere? If people share the room, can I combine their colour preferences in a scheme that pleases everyone?

ADDING COLOUR

Apart from paint and wallpaper, there are many ways to add colour to a room. Some elements have the advantage of being easily removable, allowing you to vary the look of the room season by season or simply when you desire a change.

- **light** – coloured window glass, hanging crystals, coloured bulbs, coloured candles, lightbox or projector

- **walls** – hanging fabrics, posters, paintings, wall-mounted candle-holders or light fittings, your own artwork, hand-painted tiles

- **floors** – rugs, fitted carpets, other floor coverings such as linoleum or natural seagrass, hand-painted tiles

- **objects** – painted furniture, vases, bowls and china pieces, flowers, coloured throws over furniture, cushions, curtains, tablecloths, a movable wooden screen with mounted coloured paper

colours for energy and stimulation

For an environment that will stimulate and energize you, choose reds, oranges and rich yellows. Red is the colour of blood, of types of earth and flowers, of rich dark wine. It has the power to boost the circulation and quicken the pulse. It is also the colour of warning lights, stop signs and fire engines – it can grab your attention and trigger action.

COLOURS OF NATURE

Natural materials are an effective complement to bright energizing colours. Try offsetting a red or orange wall or alcove with a sofa covered in a throw of unbleached beige-to-cream cotton or contrasting deep yellow walls with the natural grey-green of collected rocks.

Pale wood flooring is effective in offsetting many hot colour schemes, not least those dominated by rich red walls or rugs. Conversely, warm, energetic

colours make a delightful background if you want to display a treasured object such as a stone carving or a neutrally coloured statue.

RED

Red stimulates conversation and debate, and makes people feel 'alive'. For this reason, red is a favourite among designers in schemes for fashionable bars. Red also encourages activity – so it is perfect for areas where people must be kept moving, such as hotel lobbies. In the home, red can be an excellent colour for small hallways or corridors – areas where people may be energized by the colour as they pass through. Equally, red is recommended for cloakrooms

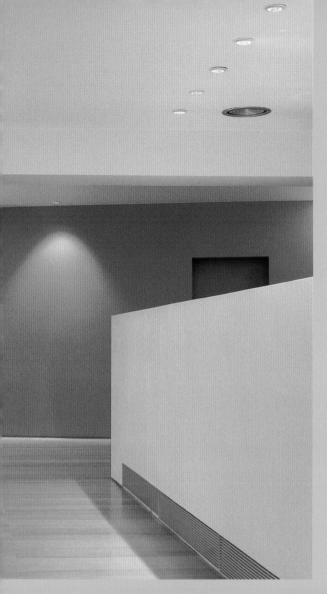

or other small rooms visited in passing. Another benefit of rich reds is that they have the effect of making a room seem warmer, so they can be a good decorative choice for cold rooms tucked away at the back of a house.

YELLOW

Radiant full yellows are suggestive of sunlight, and bring an optimistic and fresh feel to a room. Yellow is also associated with mental activity, with analytical thought and the activities of the ego. It makes a good colour for a wall in a study or in an area where children do homework.

Yellow is also suitable for rooms used in the morning, such as kitchens or breakfast rooms. Red and yellow together create a welcoming glow, and are therefore an effective combination in a well-lit hallway.

ORANGE

Orange combines red and yellow – it can be seen as a balancing colour that mixes the earthy passion of red with the mental force of yellow. Glowing orange, the colour of flames – whether in its earthy, autumnal shades such as rust and terracotta or in its lighter pure orange or peach tints – can boost people's enthusiasm and give them a sense of get-up-and-go. Orange is the colour of the sacral chakra (see page 112), which is associated with part of the digestive system, and it therefore tends to stimulate appetite. Orange is often used in restaurants and, if carefully balanced with complementary colours, may be a good choice for a dining area in the home.

Orange also stimulates movement, so it would be a good choice for an exercise room. If you are holding a party that involves dancing, add orange to your colour scheme – in the form of coloured bulbs, a bright throw over furniture or an orange rug.

MAGNETIC MIXES

If you are using large areas of the warming magnetic colours, look for colours to complement them and offset their energy.

- **red** – complemented by lavender, turquoise, blue and gold
- **yellow** – complemented by violet, lavender, blue and green
- **orange** – complemented by indigo, blue and grey

FENG SHUI COLOURS

The ancient Chinese science of feng shui teaches the right arrangement of rooms and colours at home to boost your chances of achieving fulfilment, long life and worldly success.

According to feng shui, **red** is a colour of happiness, energy and emotion, **yellow** represents spiritual and intellectual activity while harnessing understanding, and **orange** is connected to communal activities and group achievements.

COLOUR ACCENTS

Stimulating colours are often best used in small areas as accents. A light shade of a complementary colour applied in large blocks will provide a background against which a dark red or russet orange, for example, can 'lift' a room.

- the greater the contrast between accent and background colour, the smaller the area of accent should be

- use shades of **blue** and **grey** to complement **orange** and **turquoise**, or a darker **green** to complement **red**

- paint an alcove or one part of a wall in an energizing colour and the rest in a complementary colour

- try painting the wall behind a bookshelf a warm **red** or the inside of a cupboard **scarlet**

- hang **red** or **orange** drapes in a window so that daylight is coloured and further energized as it enters the room

- add contrasts in the form of furniture, vases, bowls, cushions or fresh fruit

We can have too much red, yellow or orange. Warm colours in abundance can overstimulate the nervous system – leading to feelings of uneasiness or even anger and aggression. A meeting held in a room decorated with large areas of red or orange may degenerate into disagreement and conflict, whereas one in a cool blue or dark green space is more likely to reach a productive conclusion. If you decorate your bedroom in yellow, a colour of clear-thinking and mental activity, you may find yourself stimulated at a time when you need to rest.

Moreover, like other warm colours, reds and oranges tend to move towards the viewer, so will make a room seem smaller. This might not be a problem in a corridor or cloakroom, say, where you may not be concerned if the space appears small, but large areas of red or orange are generally inadvisable in a small sitting room. You can reduce this effect by introducing a counterbalancing colour on the ceiling and on the floor – in the form of carpet, painted boards or rugs. If one or more walls are decorated in rich, energizing colours, a pale-coloured floor and ceiling provide light relief.

ROOM FOR REDS

If you want to use larger areas of energetic red, vibrant yellow or intense orange in a decorative scheme, pick your room with care. For example, such use of colour is often inappropriate in a bedroom, although some tones of red create a sensuous atmosphere (see page 60). Likewise, in a bathroom a soothing marine or green colour scheme is more conducive to relaxation.

Energizing colours can be effective in a hallway, cloakroom or lavatory, depending on the light available and how dark the

paints are. They should be used with care in small living rooms, but reds and oranges can be very effective as accent colours.

Welcoming butter yellows are perhaps better than fiery reds in kitchens, where you are unlikely to want to add to the heat, but rich reds and oranges are desirable and well-established choices for dining zones. Yellows are ideal for studies or other areas where mental work takes place; brighter shades of red might be too stimulating, but warm terracotta and rust colours may have the right degree of energizing lift.

When working with these colours, it is important not to overdo it. Large sweeps of red and orange are probably best avoided if you have high blood pressure or a heart condition because the colours, particularly red, are known to stimulate blood circulation. A shade of pink, in which the energizing red has been toned down by white, would provide a safer level of stimulation.

A PLACE TO CONCENTRATE

The capacity of **yellow** to stimulate thoughts, banish drowsiness and foster attentiveness makes it an ideal colour for a home study. If your work is creative, try introducing **violet**, the colour of intuition, to balance the power of yellow.

A kitchen painted yellow is a welcoming haven for a family, helping everyone to gather their wits in the morning, and also provides a good spot for homework.

colours for romance

The colour pink evokes romantic love, flower-scented arbours and intimate spaces where we can take refuge from the cares of the world. It is a soothing hue associated by colour theorists with compassion and the gentle treatment of self. In the making of pink, white tones down the energy and stimulation represented by red.

PEACEFULNESS AND LOVE OF HOME

A pink-themed room may help to defuse conflict, encouraging a relaxed and loving approach, while in a red room anger may be more common. But pink does not foster weakness or loss of self-respect; on the contrary, it is linked with a well-developed sense of justice, of right and wrong. Although pink suggests a person who shows unconditional love, it does not imply that such a person is weak. Pink contains the strength and life and earthiness of red.

Colour theorists say that rose-pink tones are an ideal choice for people who revel in home life, consolidating the love of home as a place of nurturing and growth. Children often favour pink instinctively; graduated pinks may be a good colour scheme for those who wish to express their romantic personality through love of partner and family. Peach pink,

A FEMININE COLOUR?

Pink is often identified as feminine in contrast to the more masculine vibrancy of **red**. Pink remains a traditional choice for nurseries and baby girls' clothes, which may explain its resonance as a colour of safety and unconditional love.

Whether you are male or female, choosing pink tends to indicate that you take pleasure in and derive confidence from your feminine side. You are not afraid to be intuitive or make yourself vulnerable by opening your heart and expressing tenderness.

which combines pink and orange, is warmer and more physical in its associations, while mauve pink, a mixture of blue and pink, is cooler and more spiritual.

Creamy white, the colour of lilies and white roses, conjures images of a summer room where gauzy curtains flutter in the breeze. Try using several tones of unbleached, creamy white offset by reddish pink, purple, red-mauve or magenta.

THE RIGHT LIGHT

Appropriate lighting is a crucial part of achieving a romantic effect. Candlelight, which like sunlight contains the full wealth of spectrum colours, casts a delicate glow on walls. Candelabra on a table create an intimate atmosphere for dinner. A room with many candles, perhaps in reds and greens, has a delicate, magical quality and makes a guest feel warmly welcomed.

Low lighting with red or pink-tinged bulbs contributes to an intimate atmosphere even in a functionally decorated room. Using coloured bulbs and a few cushions, you can create an enticing pink-to-magenta ambience, say, in a white room that might appear harsh or utilitarian in daylight – ideal for a 'chillout room' at a party.

Red, pink or violet translucent window hangings make good use of daylight, introducing a romantic colouring into a space. A room lit in this way is a haven, filling people with a gentle

dose of colour energy and helping them to set their busy minds at rest. Hanging coloured-glass beads or standing coloured-glass vases on the windowsill creates a few moments of immediate beauty when the sun shines, touching us with an intense experience of the here and now.

MODERN PINKS

To some modern tastes, traditional pinks may seem washed-out or wishy-washy, but pink comes in many more lively tones. Shocking magenta pink and lighter sugar pink have an insistence and vibrancy that can make them tiring to live with, but used with care they produce a burst of joy, a splash of heartening pleasure. Magenta, which combines red and violet, has an elevating spiritual aspect when used with restraint. But some of us seek an ambience that ignores restraint and indulges excess – such as in a highly romantic and contemporary combination of pink, deep reds and touches of orange.

SENSUOUS REDS

Deep red, the colour of the heart and of desire, can arouse passion; a red wall or red accents in a more gentle colour scheme quicken the emotions and move ardent feeling to expression.

Colour theorists advise against having red in a bedroom because it is said to be too stimulating for a place of repose. But colour tastes are highly individual – and red's associations with sensuous pleasure encourage some people to use it in the bedroom, where it can be expected to conjure feelings of intimacy and physical abandon.

Avoid bright reds; if a room is small, be wary of emphasizing its limited dimensions. Skilful placement of mirrors and use of natural and electric light can counter a shrinking effect.

RED AND MAGENTA

Red and magenta speak to us at opposite ends of our physical continuum. Red is the colour

associated with the base chakra at the bottom of the spine, while magenta flows to the crown chakra at the top of the head (see page 112). Red links us to our environment, energizing and warming our bodies; magenta lifts us from the physical to the spiritual, feeding our soul.

THE ROMANCE OF THE EXOTIC

The deep tones of Indian terracotta, the lift of bright Mexican blue and the warm sandy ochre of northern Africa suggest the excitement of the unfamiliar. These colours derive from natural pigments used largely undiluted under fierce local sunlight. In northern areas, where light is more diffused, we may want to tone down their brightness, but colour schemes based on these evocative colours have an instant exotic appeal.

A bedroom with terracotta walls and rich red bed coverings offers a safe retreat, evoking the idea of a cosy place of recuperation such as a burrow or cave. Potted houseplants, a few mantelpiece ornaments and the colour range of books on a bookcase add contrast.

Another way to introduce an exotic touch into your home is to buy imported patterned tiles and set them in the floor in front of your fireplace or put them in your bathroom or kitchen. You can also paint your own tiles in Moroccan or other evocative patterns using ceramic paints.

WATER AND LIGHT

The play of light on water is a source of fascination and delight. Try floating night lights in a large bowl of water or standing coloured candles behind a large goldfish bowl so that they are visible through the water.

EFFECTS OF COLOURED LIGHT

Colour therapists warn against using green-tinted light in the home, arguing that it does not help us to thrive. But other tinted lights can have positive effects.

- **rosy pink light** – intimate and seductive

- **red light** – stimulating and energizing (for example, the effect of daylight passing through a red gauze hanging)

- **blue light** – very soothing

- **violet light** – promotes peace, gentleness

- **golden yellow light** – provides an uplift, bringing happiness

DARK BLUE CALM

Dark blue can be used to introduce an oasis of
calm in a place where patience may run short or tempers
fray. Perhaps you have a home office and occasionally
host work meetings there – a blue area of wall, a blue
partition or a predominantly blue work of art will provide
an injection of cool. Equally, a dark blue fridge, cupboard
or piece of stained glass might be enough to soothe
a stressed cook in the kitchen.

colours for soothing
and relaxation

Green promotes healing and harmony. Except for its very yellowy lime
shades, green is restful on the eye; combining yellow and blue, it is
a colour of balance, associated with the heart chakra (see page 112)
and feelings of self-acceptance and security.

At times of loss, or when we are feeling bruised following a failed love
affair or suffering a sense of rejection in the world of work, a green room or
a green area in a room offers natural regeneration and a saving, bolstering
influence. Green provides balance, but also needs to be balanced itself. Too
much green can be stultifying - you can be soothed too much, and end up
slipping into lethargy and indolence.

HEALTHY LOOK

Colour theory links **turquoise** and other **blue-greens** to cleanliness, to a germ-free environment offering immunity from infection. However, the further our colour scheme goes towards **green**, the more we risk recalling 'hospital green', a sterile colour lacking in warmth and character.

SINGING THE BLUES

Deep blue is a calming colour for a bedroom ceiling. Add accents in bright colours – in a child's room, for example, you could paint yellow, white or orange stars on the ceiling to emulate the heavens. Daytime sky or water blues on the walls complement this colour combination, and graduating the movement from dark blue to lighter blues – by adding increasing amounts of white to the ceiling blue – makes an entrancing effect at the edge of the ceiling and down the walls.

Blue is a colour of rest, making it an excellent stress-buster after a hard day's work. As well as soothing the mind, it encourages muscular relaxation and settled breathing. Colour therapists recommend blue for the treatment of insomnia and the prevention of nightmares. A headache brought on by overwork or worry and tension will gradually ease in a predominantly blue room. Indeed, the majority of people – just over 50 per cent – name blue as their favourite colour, evidently cherishing its restful, nurturing qualities.

SOOTHING LIGHT

The colours in light have a deeper and more penetrating effect than pigments used in paint. Light makes an impact unconsciously, directly on the body cells, whereas paint colours affect only the conscious mind. Coloured lights can be powerfully soothing in milder colour schemes.

Blue-greens have a cooling effect – delightful in a well-lit space or a hot climate, but perhaps inadvisable in a cold, north-facing room. Turquoise and other marine blues, with their hint of sea-pools, summon a profound calm. They are both relaxing and lively, gentle but full of impact.

Lighter blues, greens and tints of turquoise retreat from the eye, making a small room appear bigger. They draw us into expansive thought, perhaps encouraging self-sufficiency – for this reason, they may need spicing up with warm, magnetic colours.

Marine blues open up space, making them an ideal choice for a very small room such as a cloakroom or shower room.

YELLOW AND BLUE

Yellow and blue make a soothing combination that works well in any room. From the palest of yellow and sky blue to the deepest buttery orange-yellow and dark blue, this restful, healing colour scheme lifts the spirits.

Yellow walls in a kitchen make the most of available light and blend harmoniously with the warmth of a table, floor covering or worktop in natural wood, while blue accents add interest. The colours soothe frazzled nerves when the oven is pumping out heat, the kettle whistling and the baby screaming for attention. Stainless-steel equipment and fittings satisfactorily complement blue walls.

A yellow and blue combination in a bathroom suggests a sun-drenched seascape and will help to ease you into a calm, meditative frame of mind for a healing soak in the bath.

GROUNDING COLOURS

Deep and tan browns, natural greens, wood tones, brick, terracotta, stone and unbleached white-cream all bolster the feeling of belonging to the earth. Surrounding yourself with these colours should give you a strong sense of being in your natural environment.

AMBIVALENT AUBERGINE

Aubergine combines the earthy comfort of **brown** with the luxury of **purple**.
Depending on the proportion of these colours in the mix, and the ambient
lighting, aubergine can be restful or slightly more energetic. Both tones
sit nicely with a sophisticated look – they go well with fireplaces, candlesticks,
picture- and mirror-frames and ornaments in **silver** and **gold**, and their
richness complements velvet curtains or throws. **Cream** or **white** walls
offset the deep, relaxing tones of aubergine cushions or upholstery.

Brown suggests simplicity, self-control and commitment. It is the colour of the robes traditionally worn by Catholic monks of the Franciscan order. An easy and satisfying way to introduce brown into your home is to use natural wood. Floors, ceilings, wall panels, door frames, chairs, tables, chests of drawers, bookcases and picture frames can all be marshalled to add grainy texture and shades of earthy brown to your décor.

Grey, another colour often adopted for monastic habits, is a soothing, balancing agent – both with light, bright hues such as orange and with darker browns. The natural grey of pebbles and stones often contains veins and spots of other colours.

When working with greys and browns, it is advisable to stick to natural materials – wood, wool, leather, stone – since these colours can seem rather heavy when used as pigments in paint.

There is a tendency for soothing colour schemes in brown and cream or brown and stone to appear a little impersonal, to suggest a neutral elegance of the kind sometimes adopted in rental apartments or hotels. In a home setting, browns may need to be lifted with brick-orange or light creams to make a

pleasing combination. Add a dash of colour with flowers, peacock feathers, crockery, cotton or woollen throws or a vibrant rug.

Terracotta brings warm, earthy tones to a soothing colour scheme, providing a rosy glow that offers a gentle lift of red. Mixed from natural pigments, it has a traditional feel but also a touch of the exotic, evoking as it does rich Indian and other oriental decorative schemes (see page 61). Combining terracotta with yellows and rich gold generates a welcoming, comfortable atmosphere; terracotta is a wonderful choice for north-facing rooms that receive a whiteish light, since it introduces a cosy pink warmth.

PASTEL APPROACHES

The muted tones of pastels create a light, gentle atmosphere evocative of a seaside cottage or a garden summerhouse. Soft blues, pinks, mauves, turquoises and greens, teamed with white, make the most of the light in even the gloomiest or chilliest of rooms. A touch of grey introduces a note of distinction if you want to prevent a colour scheme from becoming too pretty.

Pastel checks in blue and white are a traditional favourite for chairs and cushions in a predominantly white room. Pink and white and floral patterns add gentle warmth. You may be drawn to the cottagey look and feel it is a well-tried and appropriate way to use these colours. A more modern, urban angle would be to marshal pastels in single-colour blocks painted on white or cream walls. This provides a pleasing and distinctive, but still gentle, double act. Pastels and white are a relaxing combination because they do not set up a strong contrast, making them restful to look at.

According to the Chinese science of feng shui, pastel tints significantly affect our wellbeing. Pale blue and minty green are linked with relaxation, pink with youthfulness and play, lavender with the joy of company, and magnolia with peace.

WHITE

A colour scheme based on white offers a fresh environment suggestive of wide expanses of empty air or countryside blanketed in snow. Some people find white soothing because it delivers a sense of blankness and emptiness – they rejoice in feeling free and in having the space to be themselves. In colour theory, white is associated with innocence, neutrality, cleanliness and wisdom. If you are confused and in need of time to sort out your thoughts, you may benefit from living in a white environment. White also has undeniable elegance and can be pleasingly complemented by glass furniture and bright fittings. But white is also the colour of solitude – use too much white and you risk making yourself feel isolated. There are many whites to choose from, ranging from shades of creamy-yellow to those of grey or orange-pink; avoid blue-undertone whites, which can be extremely chilly.

BLOCKS OF COLOUR

Painted effects on walls add interest to a room. Blocks of contrasting colour derived from the **blue-green** palette and given a gentle, washed appearance bring easy, soothing movement. But be careful with bold patterns in brighter colours, stripes and horizontal lines. They tend to have a more insistent, energizing effect than would be desirable in a room intended for relaxation.

BLACK

When combined with the right colour accents, black can be a powerful decorative hue. In colour theory, black is the colour of knowledge and humble thinking. But it is also associated with being negative, and black interiors can seem depressing. The Chinese say that black in the home is lucky and tend to combine it with bright shades of red.

Black certainly needs to be handled sensitively, supported with warm-toned neutral colours and energized with red or bright green. Choose the surface treatment with care – black gloss produces a shiny finish that brightens the overall effect by reflecting light. Consider coating part of a wall or the inside of a toilet door in blackboard paint and providing chalks for guests and family members to write reminder notes, schedules and graffiti.

SILVER AND GOLD

Subtle touches of silver and gold will add elegance and opulence to a soothing colour scheme. Gold, traditionally a colour of wisdom and plenty, combines particularly well with warm reds and oranges, whereas silver, which projects serenity and knowingness, offsets cool blues and greens.

colours for meditation

A meditative colour scheme should help us to turn off our mental clock. Energizing colours such as red appear to make us more aware of time and our physical being, while blue, green, indigo, violet and magenta lift us away from the cycles of time towards the spiritual plane.

Violet and magenta are usually best limited to accents – with violet, perhaps in an earthy-yellow colour scheme, and with magenta in a largely blue combination. Add small amounts of these uplifting colours through cushions, rugs, a large vase, a floral display, paint on a chimney breast or small bookcase or the frame of a mirror.

GREEN AND BLUE

Colours such as green and blue, which are closely associated with the natural world, give us the strength to remain grounded in and embraced by

NATURAL ACCENTS

Look for natural items to add warm accent colours to your meditative colour scheme – for example, pottery, flowers, rush flooring, rugs, unpainted natural wood, candles, paintings and devotional objects, a bamboo chair, a fruit bowl, or 'found' objects from a city skip or a walk on the beach.

the physical realm as we move closer towards a state of greater spiritual calm. Green is regarded as a colour of compassion. In its darker tones, it attracts us into a spiritual oasis, a place of understanding and generosity. Blue gently stimulates creativity, encouraging imaginative thought: once we feel relaxed and grounded with blue, we can apply our minds with detachment to the problems confronting us. Blue relieves anxiety and builds self-confidence; it suggests the infinity of space, lifting us from the dense physical world towards violet and magenta and the weightless realm of the spirit.

INDIGO AND VIOLET

Indigo is associated with the brow or third eye chakra, situated between and just above the two eyes. Deep indigo evokes the

GREEN CONTRASTS

A small splash of **magenta** makes an enlivening contrast with **emerald green**. Another spiritual colour, **violet**, also works to draw out green and stimulate higher thinking processes.

wide expanses of the midnight heavens and the fathoms of sea beneath. It is linked to the freedom and release of non-logical thinking – the deep wisdom of a truth grasped by intuition. Indigo mixes well with pink and orange, and colour theory teaches that these combinations can help to free us from fear.

Violet, which adds the energy of red to blue, is the colour of the crown chakra at the top of the head and is believed to promote spirituality while bolstering self-respect and dignity. The colour is calming and gently uplifting; it soothes the soul, but also awakens higher mental processes, encouraging us to take time out to relax but also to use the time well. A violet wall or violet accents in a room will lift the spirits of somebody sitting in the room, perhaps prompting that person to step back from the daily routine and reconnect to the inner self.

Violet, like purple, combines feelings of luxury and inspirational mystery – evoking imperial purple or the spiritual elevation of bishops and archbishops. Blue shades of the colour, on the cool side of violet, appear to recede; an area of soothing blue-violet may ease the anxieties of people who suffer from claustrophobia.

GOLDEN GLOW

Warm colours such as orange and red have strong religious associations, making them appropriate for a meditative scheme.

- religious ecstasy is often depicted as the touch of **orange-red** heavenly flames

- as a colour of joy, and of some Buddhist monks' robes, **orange** has a spiritual dimension; in some contexts it is linked with the physical appetites of hunger and, through the sacral chakra, the libido – but it can also be spiritually uplifting

- **orange** is known to promote feelings of acceptance, which are helpful for the peace and detachment that aids meditation and reflective, intuitive thought

- the glow of **golden** light is associated with revelation in religious art, where it is often the colour of saintly haloes or bursts of heavenly brightness

- while too much **yellow** boosts intellectual activity and stimulates the ego, rich yellow counterbalanced by a cool **green-grey** or **light blue** adds warmth and expansiveness to the quiet of a meditative colour scheme

MAGENTA

In colour theory, magenta, the red-violet hue associated with the crown chakra (see page 112), is linked with choice and the processes of spiritual transformation. Magenta has the power to encourage change, the letting go of habits and fears, the movement into freedom. It summons the perfection we may touch or seek in meditation and other religious activity. Magenta combines wisdom gleaned from experience with spiritual aspiration.

A SPACE FOR REFLECTION

When we meditate or think reflectively, we are seeking to turn away from the stream of sensory input and calm the ceaseless chatter of our thoughts. A space for meditation or quiet reflection needs to be soothing on the eye, its colours combining to encourage a settled concentration on the inner self. Predominantly cool colours in a room are good if you want to avoid too much physical stimulation. But accents and small areas of warm colour are necessary to prevent the space appearing cold and uninvolving – we often need a lift to help us to move on from one stage to the next.

ACHIEVING DEEP CALM

It is easy to become trapped in an unproductive cycle of thought, replaying in the mind past insults or triumphs in a way that works against our better judgment and keeps us in thrall to the past. Watching the play of natural light on a sky-blue or violet wall can help to calm such niggling thoughts and anxieties. Cool tones such as peacock blue have a deep and expansive feel; they appear infinitely deep as they attract attention, yet they also encourage us to forget our physical being and shift our focus inwards.

Pastel blues warmed by creamy yellows and energized by fern green make a gentle combination. Deep blues and indigo are said to be the best colours for meditation; a powerful if very individual approach might be to combine them with violet and purple-mauves, perhaps adding energy with touches of rich red. This would be a rather dark scheme, but would work for a retreat room given plenty of natural light and the added warmth of electric lamps.

By contrast, light pistachio and other yellow-greens are cool and elegant, with a certain finesse; natural wood flooring or furniture adds warming orange contrasts, while darker green, perhaps in a sofa covering or set of curtains, brings depth and definition.

Generally, simplicity is the key for a meditative effect. A monochrome colour scheme – several tones of the same colour – may work well here. A scheme incorporating several shades of blue from palest sky blue to the deep blues of indigo would provide the right level of variety. Some contrasts in warmer, buttery orange yellows would add lift. Avoid patterns that may work against the dreamy quality that supports reflection and retreat.

THE JOY OF NEW LIFE

Relaxing **sky blue** or **white**, the
colour of wisdom, can contain the
same lift and challenge as **lime**,
the most vibrant tone of green,
which is traditionally associated with
the joy of new life in spring.

colour in your garden

your style of garden

What do you long for in a garden? A burst of colour to refresh or calm you, a green and shady spot in which to unwind, a fertile vegetable patch, a heady sweep of floral fragrance to carry you away in memory or fantasy and help you to forget your cares?

In your garden you are touched by the restorative power of nature – simply by being in full-spectrum natural light, by experiencing the soothing cycles of the days and seasons, by receiving the natural colour healing of flowers and foliage. Moreover, nature's healing benefits reach out to you in any type of garden, whether you have an expansive lawn with well-established trees, a small neat square of green, a patio behind a terraced house or a roof garden outside an upper-storey flat.

When I moved from a flat to a terraced house with a diminutive patio garden, I was struck by the soothing power of the garden despite its small size – I felt a great benefit merely from being able to sit outside beneath the sky, to inhale the fragrance of the honeysuckle that a previous householder had planted, and on a summer's evening to watch the shift of colours in the heavens and the effects of evening light on the flowers and bushes.

WHAT KIND OF GARDEN DO YOU WANT?

The first step to achieving a therapeutically colourful garden is to decide your priorities. Identify the most appealing garden style and features from this list.

- a **wild garden** – wild grasses and flowers

- a **kitchen garden** – vegetable plot and herb garden

- a **combination** of vegetable patch and lawn; you may want a hedge or fence to divide up the garden

- a **place to look out at** from inside the house; as is often the case with small urban gardens, your main concern may be to have a pleasing vista from your dining table

- a **pond** with frogs and fish; a fountain or other water feature

- a **place for children to play**; you will want, if possible, to keep delicate flowers and bushes away from areas in which ball games may be played

- a **place for pet animals**

- a **naturalized garden**, one in harmony with the environment; if you live near the sea, say, find room for driftwood and other found objects

- a **rock garden**

- a **place to sit** at your ease – for instance, in a deckchair on the lawn

- a **place to dine** – on a paved area

If you live in a town or city and your plot is small or hemmed in by other houses, you can still have the deep satisfaction of planning your garden for year-round colour and of seeing your hard work in planting and pruning rewarded – say, by a glorious display of pure white, deep red and glorious yellow against calming green foliage.

But the kind of garden you have to start with determines the strategy for achieving the effects you want. While you will be searching for potted plants, climbers and trees when planning a patio or roof terrace, you may want to consider planting large banks of flowers or buying in mature trees for a country garden. You also need to consider the prevailing conditions. Does your garden receive evening or morning sunlight? Is the soil well drained? Is it a windy spot? Do frosts come often?

TIPS FOR A SMALL GARDEN

With careful planning, you can achieve a wonderful variety even in a small city garden or roof terrace.

- **red**, **yellow** and **lilac**
  Plant colourful combinations such as tulips, hyacinths and crocuses in earthenware pots or stone troughs and store in corners, then bring into full view when ready to flower.

- **white flowers** Grow climbers such as honeysuckle or winter-flowering jasmine on a patio wall or small garden fence or on the back wall of your house.

- **violet**, **red** and **yellow**
  Put up a wall basket or hanging basket of petunias, marigolds, geraniums and trailing lobelia on the wall above a roof terrace.

- **green flavour** Grow herbs such as mint, chives or oregano in a window box.

- **red dash** Try raising cherry tomatoes in a window box or sunny patio corner. You could fashion an inexpensive greenhouse lean-to if you have space.

garden colour design

Each garden colour has its own spiritual quality and healing energy. Gardeners usually seek to create colour contrasts and harmonies, but you may want to plant a corner or window box in a single hue in order to benefit from a sizable dose of that colour's energy.

COLOUR CHOICES

Reds introduce vibrancy and visual drama to any garden. Large areas of red tend to dominate or overwhelm, but they can be balanced by green foliage. A dash of red is a fortunate addition to a garden in winter – on a cold day, red gladdens the spirit and quickens the heart.

Blues suggest peace, the calm of an empty sky or a wide stretch of water. In plants, they range from gentle pastel sky-blues to deep purple-blues; an area of blue in your garden or on your roof terrace will provide an oasis of healing calm.

Pinks soothe anxieties. A few minutes spent contemplating the pink blossom on a cherry tree or a window box of pink blooms will immerse you in this gentle colour vibration, which draws out an accepting and loving attitude. If you are tense or irritable, pinks will help you be kinder to yourself and others.

Lavender, indigo and lilac colours elevate the spirit, inspiring you to free yourself from damaging habits that keep you in thrall and to seek the guidance of your higher self. If you meditate in a room with a garden view, plant indigo colours where you can gaze on them from your meditation corner. Indigos and violet-mauves will – like pinks – help you to cope with and overcome tension and anxiety.

An array of white flowers against a bank of green leaves provides a cooling, calming touch of purity, a respite from a busy, noisy life. They suggest the serenity of the moon; some release a heady scent that emphasizes this otherworldly quality. Make yourself a white-flowered garden corner for a summer evening retreat, a place where you can recharge your batteries and find tranquillity of spirit.

GARDEN SYMBOLS

In the Chinese tradition, **red** flowers signify happiness, business achievement and success in a new venture, and a garden with vibrant **green** leaves and deeply coloured flowers ushers in prosperity and joy, but a neglected and dried-out flowerbed is a portent of unhappiness and meagre times.

Yellows are associated with spring, when we look for the tones of daffodils and primroses to signal the end of winter and a new start. These gentler yellows combine very well with silver or white flowers. Richer golden yellows are generally best marshalled in small areas of the garden, since they can overwhelm other colours. A view of yellow flowers from your study or sitting room boosts vitality and fosters alertness.

Green soothes bruised emotions and aids relaxation. People recuperating from a setback or illness find gentle healing in a day spent pottering in the garden. The many shades of green – an expanse of green lawn, an undulating wall of leaves, a bank of foliage behind flowers – provide intriguing single-colour contrasts for the eye. Green complements any other colours you choose for your palette, bringing structure and balance to the garden scheme.

Orange flowers can lift your levels of activity and your mood, and are therefore recommended for anyone suffering from lethargy or depression. They bring a warm blaze of brightness and colour energy to a chilly or gloomy garden.

THE SINGLE-COLOUR GARDEN

If you plant your entire garden in one predominant colour, you will need to make the most of varieties of shape, tone and texture. Add highlights of other colours to create visual movement and depth.

A city garden planted predominantly in green creates a deeply peaceful retreat, summoning the atmosphere of a country idyll and suggesting the depths of reflective thought stimulated by the harmonizing energy of green.

A white-themed garden – planted with silver, grey and white against a background of deep green – creates a soothing and elevating atmosphere.

Frequently, a garden's single-colour effect works best when it comes as a surprise or is revealed suddenly – for instance, if a bank of white or red flowers is hidden around a corner in your garden or shielded from general view by a bank of foliage, a tree or a garden building. Such an arrangement offers no distant view; each time you come upon the group of plants, you are forced to take them all in at once.

combining garden colours

Very few gardeners want more than an isolated burst of single-colour effects. For most of us, the art lies in mixing colours in ways that create intriguing contrasts and a pleasing overall effect. When devising a colour palette, we consider shades and tints of colours, different textures and shapes, colour in foliage, berries, fruits, grasses, garden furniture, walls and light effects as well as in flowers.

Like an artist at an easel, we think of the whole picture – for the effect of colours may vary when they are placed side by side. Plot your colour combinations in a pot or tub, within a particular flowerbed and across the entire garden.

PLANNING CONTRASTS WITH THE COLOUR WHEEL

Select adjacent hues from the colour wheel (see page 15) to build harmonies of colour. Alternatively, use different tints and shades of a single colour. Pinks, violets and lilacs make a harmonious combination.

Use complementary colours to make striking contrasts, in which the two colours stand out from one another and emphasize their difference. Poppies and other deeply red flowers look very strong against green, while orange blooms trumpet their colour energy against a bed of blues.

COLOUR BLENDS

You can achieve a variety of garden effects by subtle blends of colour.

- **soothing harmonies** – combine green and white; pink, pastel blue and lilac; or pale yellow and green

- **vibrant tones** – combine red and yellow; yellow and blue; orange and blue; red and pink against green; or darker yellow and green

- **an elevating touch** – combine pink and golden yellow; yellow and violet; or violet and pink

THE WIDER ENVIRONMENT

When choosing plant varieties and colours, bear in mind your garden's wider setting. Does it overlook a sweep of countryside or border farm fields? Is it near the sea? Is it a highly enclosed urban plot? Do you have a roof terrace from which you are mainly aware of the sky?

In a country garden, consider using cultivars of local wild flowers, since these will provide a delightful visual link to the fields near your home.

In a seaside setting, use driftwood or other found objects from the beach to add interest or to build fences. Try growing cultivated forms of the heathers and flowers that add colour to local headlands.

In a city garden or roof terrace, consider the colours of surrounding buildings or the hues predominant in the urban view when choosing your colour scheme. My patio is overlooked by the cream-white walls of a small office; this colour is echoed and set off by the tiny white flowers and green foliage of the climbing jasmine at the garden's end.

Consider adding trelliswork to disguise the perimeter walls of a roof terrace and safeguard its privacy. Scented climbers and flowers will add to the sense of a sky retreat – a safe enclave that shuts out the busy world beneath.

SIMPLE EFFECTS?

Sometimes 'less is more' in creating colour combinations. A flowerbed with just two differently coloured plant varieties will make a more marked contrast than one with several varieties in shades of the same two colours.

But, if you want depth and more complex effects, then a mixture of many plant varieties will provide an enticing view, a vista of flowers that draws in the eye.

plan for change

Your garden allows you to be an artist. The space is a blank canvas, and you have all the colours of flowers, foliage, earth, wood and brickwork as your palette. But unlike a painter you have the opportunity to create an ever-changing display of colours and textures. Each season has a characteristic colour scheme – from the pinks and primrose yellows of spring through the yellow, white and bright red joys of summer to the rusty orange and reddish browns of autumn and the bare branches and white frosts of winter. Some plant colours summon the spirit of a season – yellow daffodils and forsythia in spring, towering sunflowers or fragrant roses in late summer, astonishing red maples and yellow birches in autumn, and red-berried holly and fir trees in winte

PLANT YOUR GARDEN FOR ALL-YEAR COLOUR

SPRING

COLOUR	PLANT	FLOWERING NOTES
white and pink	snowdrop (*Galanthus nivalis*)	*late winter–early spring*
	crocus (*Crocus chrysanthus*)	*late winter–early spring*
	tulip	*spring*
	iris	*early summer*
	hawthorn tree (*Crataegus laevigata*)	*beautiful blossom in late spring*
mauve	Canterbury bell (*Campanula medium*)	*late spring–midsummer*
	crocus (*Crocus vernus*)	*late winter–early spring*
yellow	daffodil	*early spring*
	evening primrose (*Oenothera missouriensis*)	*late spring–early summer*
	forsythia (shrub) (*Forsythia* x *intermedia*)	*early spring*
red-purple	magnolia (shrub) (*Magnolia liliiflora*)	*late spring*

SUMMER

COLOUR	PLANT	FLOWERING NOTES
red	dahlia (e.g. 'Scarlet Comet' or 'Alva's Doris')	*midsummer–autumn*
	freesia (e.g. *Freesia* x *kewensis* 'Madame Curie')	*late summer*
	oriental poppy (*Papaver orientale*)	*early summer–midsummer*
	gladiolus (*Gladiolus* 'Sabu')	*all summer*
pink-white	hollyhock (*Alcea rosea*)	*mid–late summer; sometimes autumn*
	belladonna lily (*Amaryllis belladonna*)	*late summer*
	azalea (*Rhododendron viscosum*)	*early–late summer*
orange	montbretia (*Crocosmia masoniorum*)	*mid–late summer*
mauve-violet	monkshood (*Aconitum wilsonii*)	*late summer to early autumn*
	echinacea (*Echinacea purpurea*)	*mid–late summer*
	sword lily (*Gladiolus byzantinus*)	*midsummer*
	Siberian iris (*Iris sibirica*)	*early summer*
	lupin (*Lupinus polyphyllus*)	*midsummer*
blue	speedwell (*Veronica spicata*)	*mid–late summer*
	African lily (*Agapanthus* 'Lilliput')	*mid–late summer*
yellow-orange	pot marigold (*Calendula officinalis*)	*late summer–early autumn*
	sunflower (*Helianthus annuus*)	*late summer–early autumn*

AUTUMN

COLOUR	PLANT	FLOWERING NOTES
pink	Michaelmas daisy (*Aster novi-belgii*)	*late summer–early autumn*
mauve	Italian starwort (*Aster amellus*)	*late summer–early autumn*
yellow-orange	African marigold (*Tagetes erecta*)	*throughout summer*
evergreen	grasses such as New Zealand flax (*Phormium tenax* 'Variegatum') or yucca (*Yucca filamentosa* 'Variegata')	
red	creeping cotoneaster (*Cotoneaster adpressus*)	*dark green-leaved shrub, bears red berries in autumn*

WINTER

COLOUR	PLANT	FLOWERING NOTES
all colours	winter pansies (e.g. *Viola* x *wittrockiana*)	*autumn–winter*
reds	rosehips (e.g. *Rosa paulii*)	
	cyclamen (*Cyclamen coum*)	*midwinter–early spring*
	red-barked dogwood (*Cornus alba* 'Sibirica')	*red stems in winter*
	red willow (*Salix alba* 'Britzensis')	*red-orange stems in winter*
white-pink	winter cherry (*Prunus* x *subhirtella* 'Autumnalis')	*white or pink flowers in winter*
white-yellow	mimosa (*Acacia dealbata*)	*silvery leaves and scented yellow flowers winter–spring*
green	holly (e.g. *Ilex aquifolium* or *Ilex* x *altaclerensis*)	*white flowers spring–early summer and autumn berries*
blue	winter iris (*Iris unguicularis*)	*autumn–early spring*
yellow	mahonia (*Mahonia* x *media* 'Charity')	*flower clusters in winter*
	Chinese witch hazel (*Hamamelis mollis*)	*flower clusters in midwinter*

water and light

The play of light adds to the vibrancy and subtlety of the colour contrasts created by the plants, trees and man-made structures in your garden. Different colours predominate in natural light at different times of day (see page 18), affecting the colour emphasis of your garden display. And the varying qualities of light during the different seasons and in various weather conditions either suppress or enhance colour effects. For example, the hazy light that is characteristic of a hot dusty summer tends to deaden or dull colours that would sparkle with freshness in the bright, clear light that follows a spring storm.

One way to enhance colour in your garden and to introduce form and structure is through the use of shade. All but the most vibrant colours will look bleached in bright sunlight, while dappled shade rests the eyes and enables them to see depth and contrast in lighter hues.

In a very sunny spot, areas of shade created by planting trees or bushes will provide contrast and definition. If your garden is too shady, cut back overhead foliage in a far corner to make an enticing area of dappled light. When light is low towards dusk or at night, create dramatic effects with candles, lanterns, torches and electric light.

The movements of dappled light and colour reflections on water add magic to the garden atmosphere. It is a joy to see the deep red of a climbing rose reflected in a still surface. In a small garden, a pond or fountain can be expensive to

WATERBORNE PLANTS

In the Chinese tradition, the lotus is a plant of summer and signifies purity of spirit. The flower, which blooms for a single day, is also the national flower of India, where religious iconography often depicts the Buddha or the Hindu god Brahma seated on a lotus flower.

An easy alternative to the lotus is to grow a water lily in a good-sized glazed pot filled with water. Keep the pot in partial shade. This is a cheap and easy way to enjoy the calming effects of water in your garden.

A GARDEN FULL OF LIGHT

There are many ways of using light to enhance your garden colour.

- **candles** set in the earth

- flame **torches**

- glass **lanterns** hanging from a tree; make your own glass lanterns using food jars, candles and wire

- chinese **paper lanterns**

- **Christmas tree lights** or larger electric string and rope lights, wound around trees and plant stalks (check that they are safe for outside use); they can also be intertwined in garden structures such as a pergola or trelliswork

- electric **spotlights**

- **night lights** in a silver bowl or floating in water in a glass container

- **candles** or night lights floating in a pond, or a spotlight trained on a garden fountain

- candles, lights or **rope lights** set in windows overlooking the garden

- a **candelabra** or selection of candles arranged on a garden table

- a **chiminea** (a clay or cast-iron wood- and charcoal-burning oven/patio heater) provides a warm glow

install and may require continuing maintenance, but there are simpler alternatives – try a birdbath, for instance, or even a glazed pot or large copper bowl filled with water.

CAMERA EYE

Take photographs of your garden in early morning and mid-morning, at noon, in mid- and later afternoon and in the dying light near dusk. Try again on another day, when the weather is markedly different. The results will reveal how particular areas appear at different times and in different weathers; they may give you ideas of ways to enhance the appearance and colour design of parts of the garden – how to bring a distant corner out of obscurity, say, or how to lead the eye across the garden in a smoother or more dramatic movement.

LIGHTER AND DARKER

The colours of your garden change as the quality of light varies at different times of day. Light colours such as **yellow** and **white** gain an intensely bright appearance under the noon sun, while darker colours are unaffected. White flowers will stand out brilliantly from **green** foliage.

In the **red** to **violet** light of sunset, dark garden hues such as **purple** and **blue** appear to grow darker as the light colours, especially white, gain a ghostly luminescence.

the soothing garden

To create a peaceful garden that offers a retreat from the busy modern world, aim for a harmonious blend of colours. Try white and pastel pink, gentle yellow, cool blue and elevating violet set against the green of foliage and long grass. Avoid hues that create strong contrasts and offer stimulation, such as vibrant reds, oranges and bright yellows.

The green of foliage and grasses provides the perfect setting for an array of peaceful colours, balancing their energies and enhancing their soothing effects. Nature's green is constant but subtly changing: it works its magic throughout the year, from the deep evergreen shades of winter and the lighter more vibrant hues of spring through dusty, sun-drenched summer greens to the dying colours of late summer and early autumn, when green fades to yellow and brown. Make room for green – if foliage is crowded out by flowers, the floral colours, however gentle, will begin to banish the sense of peacefulness from your soothing garden.

A PLACE TO SIT

Don't forget to make a place for yourself in your scheme. When planning colours and planting, consider where you will sit to take pleasure in them. Choose a spot where you can look away from the house or flat (and forget the jobs and worries associated with it) to gaze at soothing colours – and

PLANTS FOR A SOOTHING COLOUR GARDEN

pink
- alpine clematis (*Clematis alpina*)
- goat's rue (*Galega officinalis*)
- mallow (*Lavatera trimestris*)

blue
- morning glory (*Ipomoea purpurea*)
- sea holly (*Eryngium bourgatii*)
- Siberian iris (*Iris sibirica*)
- Jacob's ladder (*Polemonium foliosissimum*)

violet or purple
- lavender (*Lavandula*)
- Cupid's dart (*Catananche caerulea*)
- grassy bells (*Edraianthus pumilio*)
- allium (*Allium sphaerocephalon*)

white or cream
- arum lily (*Zantedeschia aethiopica*)
- bishop's flower (*Ammi majus*)
- summer snowflake (*Leucojum aestivum* 'Gravetye Giant')
- masterwort (*Astrantia major*)
- foxglove (*Digitalis purpurea* f. *albiflora*)

green
- lady fern (*Athyrium filix-femina*)
- alpine water fern (*Blechnum penna-marina*)
- Japanese holly fern (*Cyrtomium fortunei*)
- broad buckler fern (*Dryopteris dilatata*)
- ostrich fern (*Matteuccia struthiopteris*)

enjoy any view you may have of sky, sea or landscape beyond the garden. If you are choosing flowers for their fragrance as well as their colour, plant the sweetest-smelling ones alongside your place of refuge. For example, train a rose up the wall behind your seat or a swathe of lavender near your hammock.

Do you have a tree big enough to hang a simple swing? The soothing effects of the green, dappled shade and the array of flowerbed colours beyond will be enhanced by the gentle movement of air against your face as you swing idly back and forth.

Don't choose style over comfort in garden furniture: some of the elegant metal seats and benches on the market may not be practical – they may be too hard and angular for your body. You can add colour and comfort with cushions and drapes.

SOUND AND COLOUR

The gentle sounds of nature provide a supportive backdrop for the soothing effects of your garden colours. Contemplative thoughts are enriched by the music of water trickling in a shade-dappled stream or falling in a white spray from a fountain, the call of birds in green leaves, the drone of bees above red and yellow flowers, the rustle of the breeze in the trees against the blue sky. If you don't have a stream, fountain or tree, you can add sound to colour by planting grasses in your garden. Their whisper in a breeze at dusk will draw your eye to their delicate greens, blues and greys. Recommended grasses include needle grass (*Stipa tenuissima*), giant feather grass (*Stipa gigantea*), pheasant's tail grass (*Stipa arundinacea*), *Briza triloba* and *Carex comans*.

the vibrant garden

To create a stimulating outdoor space that will give you restorative bursts of energy, plant red, deep yellow and orange – poppies, peonies, tulips, sunflowers, montbretia and daffodils. The effect can be achieved as much by the planting as the plants themselves – a wide flowerbed of densely coloured tulips, say, with a few balancing greens, will certainly lift rather than soothe your spirits. A stand of sunflowers crowded in a sun-drenched corner or a white garden wall covered in red roses will have the same effect.

EXPRESSING YOUR ASPIRATIONS

A corner of your garden that is dominated by green, blue and pink expresses your existing sense of calm but also helps to create inner security – merely visiting the spot and drinking in the vibrations of these soothing colours will enable you to find a quiet, restorative space in a mind full of turmoil.

In the same way, more stimulating areas of colour are an expression of the levels of energy and vibrant self-confidence to which you aspire. A few moments in this bright garden corner should provide the pick-me-up you need.

A well-planned, carefully maintained plot – which includes elements of symmetry, perhaps with a pond or other water feature and harmonious use of colours – provides an example of order and stability that you can turn to when life beyond the home seems chaotic.

A more unrestrained garden landscape – with irregular plantings of wild flowers and grasses, and a backdrop of trees or shrubs – is an example of the rolling movement of the seasons, of the earth's irrepressible fecundity. If modern life seems sterile or trivial, you may find inspiration in this vision of a natural order that carries on as it always has done.

IN HARMONY WITH YOUR HOME

A naturalized garden that incorporates local wild flowers, plants that attract birds, butterflies and other wildlife, and is designed to complement its surroundings will affirm your sense of being in the right place at the right time, reminding you that you belong there and have much to offer in life.

PLANTS FOR A VIBRANT GARDEN

red
Peruvian lily (*Alstroemeria aurantiaca*)
cinquefoil (*Potentilla* 'Gibson's Scarlet')
Ricinus communis 'Carmencita'
montbretia (*Crocosmia* 'Lucifer')

yellow
daffodil, yellow tulip, sunflower
evening primrose (*Oenothera missouriensis*)
Jerusalem sage (*Phlomis fruticosa*)
Spanish broom (*Genista lydia*)
winter aconite (*Eranthis hyemalis*)

orange
canna lily (*Canna* 'Wyoming')
English marigold (*Calendula officinalis* 'Indian Prince')
California poppy (*Eschscholzia californica*)
African marigold (*Tagetes erecta*)

VIBRANT TREES AND SHRUBS

To make a dramatic impact in your garden, plant one or more of the following trees or shrubs.

- **Chilean fire bush** (*Embothrium coccineum*) – evergreen that produces scarlet-orange flowers in the first half of summer; grows up to 9 metres (30 feet) in height

- **laburnum** (*Laburnum anagyroides*) – tree that produces golden-yellow flowers in spring and summer; grows up to 4 metres (18 feet)

- **common broom** (*Cytisus scoparius*) – shrub that produces deep yellow flowers in the early months of summer; grows up to 1.8 metres (6 feet)

- **variegated weigela** (*Weigela florida* 'Aureovariegata') shrub that flowers pink in summer; grows up to 2 metres (6 feet 6 inches)

- **cinquefoil** (*Potentilla arbuscula*) – shrub that produces yellow flowers from late spring to end of autumn; grows up to 1.2 metres (4 feet)

LANGUAGE OF FLOWERS

In past centuries, lovers, friends and relatives understood the meanings associated with gifts of particular blooms. We still associate red roses with declarations of love but have forgotten many other traditional floral meanings.

- **chrysanthemums** signify friendship

- **irises** are associated with wisdom

- **white lilies** and **white violets** represent innocence

- **white carnations** mean the best of luck

- **blue forget-me-nots** and **white daisies** signify faithfulness

- **pansies** convey enduring love

- **orange blossom** and **marjoram** are linked with fertility

- **honeysuckle** means a secret love

- **marigolds** represent a shared sadness

colour all around

Colour in your garden derives not only from plants and vegetation. Consider the hues and textures of your garden walls and fences, of garden furniture, children's play equipment, sheds, decking, paving, tiles, statues, tubs, pots, areas of gravel or stones – and perhaps a summer house, tree house or birds' nesting box. All contribute to the overall colour scheme. The colours of the building in which you live – porch, window frames, shutters, roofing tiles, chimney blocks, guttering and drainpipes, window boxes, wall baskets – affect your colour response in the garden. And the colours you can see when you look out from the garden are also influential: trees or bushes on a nearby plot of land, climbing plants on your neighbour's wall, a sea or country view, or the predominant hues of an urban landscape.

NEIGHBOUR CLASH

If you live close to your neighbours, the decorative scheme on the front and back of their houses will have an impact on the way you experience colour in your garden. If your neighbour's house or paintwork clashes with your own house or garden colour scheme, consider repainting or replanting to create harmony. Alternatively, plant a climber or tree at the edge of your plot to introduce the harmonizing influence of its foliage and flowers and to dilute the colour clash.

WATER MIRROR

If you have a pool, fountain or swimming pool, the colour decisions you make in respect of tiling, fittings and surroundings will have lasting impact. Remember that still water reflects and tends to take on the colour of whatever lies above and around it – the blue of sky, the green of surrounding or overhanging trees. Shallow water will also take colour from any tiles visible through it. Try turquoise-green, blue or red-pink tiles – and plant harmoniously in the surrounding area. If you plan to illuminate a fountain with a spotlight, experiment with coloured bulbs.

FRONT APPROACH

Many of us have functional front gardens – places to park the car or store the bicycle, to keep rubbish bins and so on. A drab outlook may subtly drag you down each time you return home, or project an unwelcoming, depressing image of your home to visitors and passers-by. Consider also how well the colour of your driveway harmonizes with the front of the house, and how well any wall or fencing at the front of your property combines with the driveway, the front-garden colours and the house itself.

GARDEN ART

A statue, an arrangement of stones or a wooden carving add colour to a garden and can greatly enhance its atmosphere. Oriental busts and statues of the Buddha, a bodhisattva or some Hindu gods and goddesses bring a serene presence. Consider colour and impact when deciding where to place your artwork – a green-tinged statue clearly may not have much of an impact when set against foliage; you may prefer to stand it in a hidden place around a corner or behind an outgrowth of vegetation so that visitors to the garden come upon it unexpectedly. Sometimes you will be guided by tradition – images of the elephant-headed Hindu god Ganesha, 'Lord of the Threshold', are often set above or alongside doorways.

TREE WISDOM

According to ancient Chinese wisdom, evergreens indicate that you will be long-lived, apple trees are the sign of a safe haven and orange trees bring good luck.

ADD COLOUR TO YOUR FRONT OUTLOOK

Spice up the entrance to your home with plants, accessories or decorative touches.

- **window boxes** with seasonally changing displays
- a colourful red or green front **fence**
- brightly coloured **bins**
- a **climber** on the front wall
- an enlivening colour for the **front door** or **porch**
- **stained glass** above or within the front door or porch
- a colourful **garage door**
- a **sculpture**
- a **flowering tree** or **shrub**

colour and fragrance

The fragrance of flowers is an important part of the beauty of your garden, their heady scents bringing back happy memories, reviving the spirits and metaphorically transporting you to a peaceful, revitalizing place. You may grow some less attractive plants such as mignonette for their scent alone, but if you are seeking to combine colour and fragrance there is a wide selection of flowers to choose from.

Many beautifully scented plants have predominantly white flowers – honeysuckle, jasmine, lilies or white roses make a pleasing contrast against the green leaves of foliage or an expanse of brickwork behind. Pink sweet pea or the distinctive sweep of lavender add contrasting colour. Experiment with planting flowers that combine fragrances: lilies, roses and honeysuckle set against a green garden corner make a seductive combination of scents.

A small herb garden or a few herbs grown among flowers will enhance your blend of colours and scents – and the herbs will also be useful in the kitchen. An area of purple-flowering thyme or soothing green sage adds a new dimension to your garden, while spiky rosemary or feathery fennel make for an intriguing contrast of texture set against other plants.

You can plan your coloured and perfumed garden to deliver evocative fragrances from beautiful flowers throughout the year. In winter the scented and yellow-flowering witch hazel and wintersweet will add arresting scents and a splash of colour even on the darkest days. *Mahonia japonica* combines the appeal of reddish-purple leaves with lemon-coloured flowers and a scent that resembles lily of the valley.

If you have a large garden, plant your winter-flowering shrubs near the house or alongside a pathway that you frequently use so you will get the most from them even at times when the weather discourages you from spending much time outside.

In spring try *Daphne odora* 'Aureomarginata', which offers highly scented red-purple flowers backed by yellow-edged evergreen leaves. In later spring and early summer

try *Gardenia jasminoides*, which has white-to-yellow flowers with a sweet fragrance that are set off delightfully against the plant's glossy dark green leaves. Once again, plant these towards the front of the plot, near a path, so that you can enjoy the full effect of the fragrance.

Colourful scented flowers for summer include red-to-purple peonies, pink border phlox and creamy-white mock orange. If you take pleasure in evocatively scented walks at dusk, try pinkish night-scented stock, whose flowers open in the evening. For a beautifully scented rose, try the intensely sweet-fragranced *Rosa gallica* var. *officinalis*.

The remarkable power of scents to recall memories and evoke feelings means that you should take care when selecting plants for their fragrance. A particular scent may be enough to transport you back to a time of heartbreak or bereavement – and, if so, you would not want to be reminded of this difficult period every day in your garden. Before buying and planting, pause to consider and, if necessary, check the scents of flowers and herbs.

For maximum effect, grow scented flowers in a sunny, sheltered corner of the garden, where no breeze is likely to dissipate the perfume. If you can, visit your 'scented garden' in the morning when the dew-fresh flowers are at their most fragrant. Train plants over arches and arbours so that their scent is released above you and hangs in the air. Place a bench or chair nearby so that you can take your ease in that precious spot, bathed in the soothing and restorative combination of hues and fragrances.

PLANTS THAT COMBINE COLOUR AND FRAGRANCE

border phlox (*Phlox paniculata*)
common thyme (*Thymus vulgaris*)
Daphne odora 'Aureomarginata'
lavender (*Lavandula*)
night-scented stock (*Matthiola bicornis*)
peony (*Paeonia lactiflora*)
scented varieties of rose
sweet rocket (*Hesperis matronalis*)
wintersweet (*Chimonanthus praecox*)
witch hazel (*Hamamelis*)

colour and nutrition

food colours and a balanced diet

Colour stimulates our appetite for healthy food. Nature brings a rich array of colour to our tables: the deep red of a tomato, the violet of an aubergine, the fresh yellow of a lemon, the variegated greens of a bowl of salad leaves, the golden brown of the crust on freshly baked bread. In food preparation and nutrition – as in clothes, gardening and throughout the home – natural colours deliver goodness, healing and vitalizing energy.

COLOUR NUTRITION

Colour nutrition works by applying the spectrum of the rainbow to diet – from red and orange (red meats, peaches) through gold/yellow (rice, wholegrains, bananas) and green (lettuce, peas, kiwi fruit) to blue-violet (olives, plums, beetroot). Monitor the colour range of the foods you normally eat. If your usual foods are predominantly one colour, you probably need to broaden your diet to ensure that your body receives a well-balanced combination of nutrients.

GETTING THE MOST FROM FOOD

Eat food lightly cooked or raw to obtain the maximum benefit from its colour and nutritional content. Overcooking vegetables destroys their colour, vitamins and minerals – compare the colour of freshly grated carrot with the sliced carrots often served in mass-catering establishments. Purchase only the freshest organic ingredients to avoid unnatural chemical additives. Cook vegetables by steaming, rather than boiling, to preserve their fresh colour and nutritional goodness. Use food shortly after you buy it or pick it – if possible, bring it to your table direct from your garden or allotment. Prepare your food just before you eat it; research has shown that the longer you store prepared vegetables, say, the more it reduces their nutritional value. Finally, don't rush. Give the food your full attention as you prepare and eat it. Let your heart fill with love for the family or friends with whom you will share the meal.

THE RAINBOW COLOURS OF A BALANCED DIET

If you have a good mixture of food colours in your diet, you will maintain a balanced intake – thereby increasing your vitality and helping to safeguard your health.

- About half of food intake should be from the mid-range of the spectrum – **gold/ brown** to **green**; make up the rest with **blue/indigo**, **purple** and **red** foods

- A healthy meal will include foods that are **gold/brown**, **green** and **red/orange** – for example, chicken breast with carrots and red pepper (red/orange), potatoes (gold/brown), and broccoli with peas and beans (green). **Red** and **white** meats are usually classified as red foods

- For a balanced diet you should add some **blue**, **indigo** and **purple** foods – perhaps a fruit dish of blackberries, black cherries and red-purple grapes

- The colour nutrition scheme is easily adapted to your dietary needs – replace chicken with cheese if you are vegetarian, or with lentils if you are vegan

NATURAL OR SYNTHETIC?

Food manufacturers know how much colour appeals to us, and use bright synthetic hues to make processed foods appear appetizing – think of the garish colours of some ice creams and fast foods. In this respect, our love of colour can lead us astray. These chemical colours may be attractive, but do not necessarily provide the kind of nourishment we need. For the sake of our health, we must learn to distinguish between natural and synthetic colours.

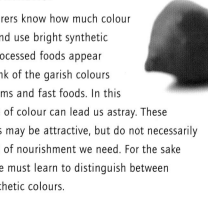

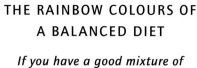

warming foods, cooling foods

Some foods have a warming and drying effect, while others are comparatively cooling and moistening. In terms of colour nutrition, warming foods are at the red end of the spectrum and cooling foods are towards the blue end. The traditional Chinese theory of yin and yang adds to our understanding of these differences.

From ancient times, the Chinese explained the universe in terms of the complementary yin and yang principles. The two principles are part of a continuum. Everything, including food and colour, is at a point on this continuum – is more or less yin or yang.

YIN	YANG
female	*male*
earth	*sky*
valley	*mountain*
passive	*active*
dark	*light*
absorbing	*penetrating*
sweet	*salty*
moist	*dry*
cool	*hot*

YIN-YANG AND COLOUR

The yin-yang continuum can be overlaid on the colour spectrum. Yin corresponds to the blue end of the spectrum and yang to red – yin is particularly linked to azure blue and yang to orange. Foods are yin, yang or 'balancing'. The balancing foods occupy a position in the centre of the continuum and are associated mainly with green. Yin foods are blue-violet foods and drinks such as honey, sugar, alcohol and milk. Balancing foods are golden yellow and green foods such as cereals, nuts, seeds and vegetables. Yang foods are red-orange foods including red meat, eggs, cheese and salt.

HEALTH FOOD

Using foods from different colour groups is one way to boost your reserves of colour energy. Try to be sensitive to your body's needs: this approach may help protect against some physical ailments – and perhaps jump-start your self-confidence and optimism to help to combat psychological difficulties such as depression. Foods from the red-orange-yellow end of the spectrum provide a warming lift and boost brainpower. Green foods bring harmony to an individual's colour energy. Blue-violet foods may ease muscular pains and soothe problems associated with constriction and anxiety.

LOOK FOR HEALTHY COLOURS

If we encourage children to take pleasure in the natural colours of the foods they eat, they are more likely to learn to associate natural colours with good tastes and to appreciate a healthy nutritional and colour balance in their diet.

FEELING BLUE?

To keep healthy and feeling our best, we need to maintain a balance of yin and yang in our body and in our diet. Too much yin may make a person feel depressed, while too much yang may be associated with overheating or heart and circulation problems. Good health depends on a balance between yin and yang. Once this balance is achieved, our body's immune system should be strong and naturally keep illness at bay.

FIVE FOODS FOR A COLD DAY

pumpkin soup
a meal made with hot spices
  such as chilli and ginger
grilled red pepper
peach
raspberries

FIVE FOODS FOR A WARM DAY

aubergine
bean sprouts
cucumber
grapefruit
banana

SINGLE-COLOUR BOOST

If you are drawn to one colour energy at a particular time, try creating a plate of food in that colour. (Colour nutritionists categorize tinned fish and milk products as green foods.)

- **green** Tuna and avocado with green beans and lettuce salad, followed by green grapes.

- **yellow-orange** Rice with yellow lentils, butternut squash and potato cooked in ginger and turmeric, followed by an orange and mango fruit salad.

- **red** Lean rare steak, red lentils, kidney beans and red peppers, served with cooked tomatoes, followed by a salad of raspberries, cranberries and strawberries.

- **blue-indigo-violet** Grilled aubergine with red-purple rice garnished with radicchio, accompanied by beetroot salad, followed by blueberries.

green foods

Green is the colour of balance. Gentle greens are linked to the heart chakra (see page 112), and associated with love, forgiveness and a sense of security, with finding a calm and even-handed way between extremes.

When we combine foods by colour, we use leafy vegetables and other green-energy sources to balance the force of foods from the red/orange/yellow group such as red meat, pasta and cheese and those from the blue/violet group such as fresh fish, mushrooms and soya. If we imagine a meal as a rainbow on a plate, then green foods are the essential middle wavelength that balances and connects the red/orange and blue/violet bands on either side.

Many vegetables and fruits clearly contain green energy – for example, cabbage, lettuce, peas, avocados, broccoli, green beans, courgettes, green peppers, brussel sprouts, green apples, grapes, kiwi fruits, limes, spring greens, and so on. But not all green-energy foods are green in colour. In addition to leafy greens and other vegetables, green-energy foods include canned fish such as tuna and sardines; olive oil, olives and nuts; tofu and some beans and pulses; and milk and yoghurt, both of which are understood to be green in origin, since animals eat grass or other green foods while making their milk.

YOUR BODY'S GUIDANCE

The most beneficial way to decide which foods to choose and how to balance their colours is to listen to your body and let it tell you what it needs. You may have to take a step out of the daily round, perhaps by embarking on a 24-hour fast or following a detox diet, in order to break the force of dietary habits that might otherwise confuse you.

Experiment with different foods and different combinations of the colour-energy groups and note the effects on your energy levels, your digestion and your overall sense of physical and spiritual wellbeing.

BENEFITS OF GREEN FOODS

Green vegetables
have a cleansing effect
on the body, making them
ideal for a natural detox. Green
foods can also have beneficial
effects on blood pressure and
stomach acidity.

On a psychological plane,
green foods
foster harmony
in life.

GREEN ENERGY: MAKE TIME FOR OTHERS

Many of us suffer from competing demands in our lives, leaving us regretful that
we cannot spend more energy on our children or on a private project that we care
passionately about. But when we can achieve colour balance, when we have an
abundance of middle-wavelength green energy, we begin to find harmony between
different parts of our life – or to understand how to bring about a harmonious
resolution to our problems. This new insight liberates time that we can then devote
to other people. Green is also the colour of love, forgiveness and self-confidence –
solidly grounded in green energy, with a healthy heart and a cooperative nature and
well-established in ourselves, we have the confidence and time to look outwards and
can make ourselves available to respond to the pressing needs of a troubled world.

GREEN REMEDY

If you are under great stress
or have recently had a nasty
shock such as an accident, you
may be in need of **green**-energy
foods. You can boost the effect
of the foods on your body and
spirit by drinking green-
energized water (see page 120)
and by wearing a green
pullover or scarf.

EAT YELLOW

In foods, **yellow** ranges from the rich shades of a banana skin or a slab of salty butter to the thinner, greener hues of lemon. Yellow foods include many staples of a healthy diet: rice, wholegrains, nuts, yellow lentils, corn, butter, lemon, banana, pineapple, melon and grapefruit.

yellow and orange foods

Someone who is feeling lethargic or depressed can be helped by a burst of the uplifting energy contained in orange and yellow foods. Try these colour vibrations if you are suffering from lack of sunlight in winter, are run down by overwork or are fearful of facing a new challenge.

Yellow is the colour of the solar plexus chakra or energy centre, which is believed by colour nutritionists to govern the body's digestive and nervous systems. The yellow colour vibration fosters clear thinking, confidence and a positive outlook. (See pages 112–14 for a full explanation of the body's chakras.)

Orange is the colour of the sacral chakra, which governs both the stomach and the reproductive system. Orange appears to enhance our appetite for food, which is why it is frequently used to decorate restaurants and is recommended as part of a balanced colour scheme for a home dining area. The colour is also believed to promote fertility. The orange colour vibration helps us to feel confident, capable, sociable and communicative.

BENEFITS OF YELLOW AND ORANGE FOODS

Many orange and yellow foods contain antioxidants, which can protect against serious disease.

- The body requires **beta-carotene**, found in carrots and in green and other orange-yellow vegetables and fruits, to make **vitamin A**. Vitamin A boosts the immune system and helps us to maintain healthy skin and eyes.

- **Vitamin A** and **vitamin C** Found abundantly in oranges and lemons, as well as in green vegetables. Important antioxidants (see page 103) that can offer protection against heart disease and cancer.

- **Vitamin E** Found in yellow foods such as wholegrains, seeds and nuts. Helps to protect against heart disease, certain cancers and other chronic ailments, and may slow the effects of ageing.

- Orange and yellow foods enhance the body's capacity to break foods down and expel waste products.

- Yellow colour energy may improve the memory as well as other thought processes.

- Orange colour energy may help us to take pleasure in life – enjoying food and social interaction, while benefiting from a healthy libido.

- The positive attitude fostered by these colours helps to protect against self-destructive patterns of thought and behaviour. Optimism and self-belief are a great benefit when we need to recover from an illness, injury or other setback.

EAT ORANGE

Fruits, root vegetables, spices and egg yolks are rich in **orange** energy. Orange foods include apricot, orange, peach, mango, potato, carrot, swede, pumpkin, butternut squash, pasta, ginger and turmeric.

red foods

Many of the most enticing fruits and vegetables are bright reds that conjure visions of a crisp and colourful alfresco lunch on a sun-baked summer's day. The many natural reds of raspberries, strawberries, red cherries, watermelon, tomatoes, radishes and red peppers bear witness to the goodness of sun-ripened, vitamin-rich food.

Red colour in food may also mean hearty winter meals of roast beef for carnivores, or platefuls of red lentils with grilled peppers for vegetarians and vegans. Meats and most other animal products are considered by colour nutritionists to be foods filled with red energy.

Red in food has a stimulating, energizing power. It is the colour of the lowest of the body's chakras or energy centres, the base chakra, situated at the base of the spine. It governs the kidneys and the system of muscles.

PROS AND CONS OF RED FOODS

Red can boost our strength and vitality, making us determined and filling us with primal energy.

HOT TOMATOES

A diet rich in lycopene – a type of carotenoid found in large quantities in cooked tomatoes – reduces a man's risk of developing prostate cancer by almost 45 per cent.

But salad tomatoes do not deliver an equivalent benefit – there is five times more lycopene in cooked tomatoes than in raw ones.

FOODS RICH IN ANTIOXIDANTS

ANTIOXIDANT TYPE	FOOD COLOUR GROUP	FOUND MOST COMMONLY IN
alpha-carotene	orange	carrots, pumpkins
beta-carotene	orange/yellow/red/green	carrots, red peppers, red and green fruits
cryptoxanthin	orange	peaches, oranges
lutein, zeaxanthin	green/red/orange	leafy greens, pumpkins, red peppers
lycopene	red	cooked tomatoes, watermelons
vitamin A	red/yellow/orange	apples, red peppers, butter, egg yolk, liver
vitamin C	red/yellow/orange/green	oranges, lemons, strawberries, cherries, red peppers, leafy greens
vitamin E	yellow	wholegrains, nuts

However, certain red-energy foods can lead to overstimulation. If we eat an excess of them, we risk becoming overexcited, short-tempered and impatient; we may find it difficult to settle to work; we may begin to rush when we should go slowly and carefully. The solution is to seek balance by adding golden yellow and green foods to the table.

Some brightly coloured fruits, such as red yew berries, are poisonous, and rotting food sometimes grows bright moulds, but the fresh colour of a fruit or vegetable usually signals that the food will help to safeguard health.

FREE RADICALS AND ANTIOXIDANTS

After every meal, as our digestive system breaks down the food we have eaten, our body produces unstable molecules called free radicals, which react with nearby molecules, setting off a process called oxidation, which can have many harmful effects on health. For example, oxidation in the blood can result in the build-up of fatty deposits, which can eventually lead to stroke or heart disease. Oxidation in the nucleus of a cell can trigger changes that lead to cancer. Research has also linked the activity of free radicals with premature ageing and the development of arthritis and cataracts.

Antioxidants are natural substances found in some foods that are used by the body as protection against free radicals. Vitamins A, C and E and carotenoids – pigments that give fruit and vegetables their deep red, yellow and orange colours – are examples of antioxidants. Eating fruits and vegetables rich in carotenoids and vitamins A, C and E gives the body plenty of antioxidants to fight disease. There are six types of carotenoid used by the body to maintain health (see chart above).

EAT BLUE-INDIGO

Blue-indigo foods have a cooling effect. They include blackberries, blueberries, bilberries, cherries, currants, fish, mushrooms, prunes, black olives and yeast.

EAT PURPLE-VIOLET

Purple-violet foods include aubergines, shellfish, oats, figs, dates, purple cabbage, radicchio, beetroot, plums, purple onions and purple broccoli.

blue, indigo and violet foods

Foods that come from the blue-indigo to violet end of the spectrum tend to have a cooling rather than a stimulating effect. Blues contain a preponderance of yin over yang energy (see page 96).

Blue food suggests first of all berries and plums – fruits such as blackberries, blueberries, black cherries, raisins and blue plums. Colour nutritionists also consider mushrooms, olives, yeast, soybeans and most fish to be blue foods.

Blue is the colour of the throat chakra or energy centre and controls the respiratory system. You may benefit from the energy of blue food if you feel confused or anxious. Blue will help you to relax and breathe more easily, delivering the confidence of self-possession and the power of imagination. Blue food energy may help you slow yourself down to a more productive speed if your anxiety is forcing you to rush things.

Purple-violet foods include aubergine, beetroot, radicchio, purple cabbage and suitably coloured plums, onions, peppers and cabbage. They mix the heating, stimulating vibration of red with the cooling, more peaceful vibration of blue to create a balanced energy that combines yang (red) and yin (blue).

Violet is the colour of the crown chakra, at the very top of the head, which controls the central nervous system (the brain and the spinal cord). The balanced red-blue energy of violet foods can alleviate stress. The violet, blue and indigo colour vibrations may ease insomnia or problems of the nerves.

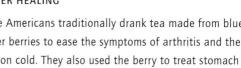

FOR YOUR NERVOUS SYSTEM

Essential acids in fish (blue) are beneficial. Eat plenty of oats (violet), which are a tonic for the nerves. Bilberries and blueberries are also recommended.

INDIGO RICE

'Purple sticky rice' from Thailand does not look very appealing in the jar but turns an attractive indigo blue once it has been cooked. The rice is usually served as a dessert in rice pudding or rice balls.

JUNIPER HEALING

Native Americans traditionally drank tea made from blue-black juniper berries to ease the symptoms of arthritis and the common cold. They also used the berry to treat stomach aches.

SPICES, HERBS AND COLOUR ENERGIES

Spices and herbs bring a wide variety of blue and other colour energies to the table through their use in cooking.

SPICE OR HERB	COLOUR	SUGGESTED USE
poppy seeds (from *Papaver somniferum*)	blue-grey	use to add nutty taste and aroma to breads, rolls, Turkish desserts
coriander (seed of *Coriandrum sativum*)	yellow-red	use in curries
ginger (root of *Zingiber officinale*)	golden yellow, brown	use in curries, ginger ale or gingerbread
sage (leaves of *Salvia officinalis*)	grey-green	use when cooking with meat, chopped in salads or with cheese
oregano (leaves of *Origanum vulgare*)	green	use in pizza and chilli powder

HERBAL HEALING

Purple-blue-indigo herbs and herbs of other colours deliver healing through their use in natural remedies.

COLOUR	HERB	SUGGESTED USE
purple-violet	hyssop (*Hyssopus officinalis*)	to treat breathing problems, help digestion, sooth skin sores
	lavender (*Lavandula officinalis*)	to treat an upset stomach
blue	juniper (*Juniperus communis*)	berries act as a diuretic
pink-red	valerian (*Valeriana officinalis*)	as a mild sedative, especially to encourage sleep
green	aloe vera (*Aloe barbadensis*)	to heal burnt skin and soften and sooth skin tissue
yellow	dandelion (*Taraxacum officinale*)	to treat liver problems or stimulate the appetite; acts as a diuretic
	evening primrose (*Oenothera biennis*)	to lower blood pressure; oil from the plant's seeds can be swallowed to treat migraine or types of asthma or eczema
yellow-white	feverfew (*Tanacetum parthenium*)	to treat headaches, insect bites or migraine
brown-green	witch hazel (*Hamamelis virginiana*)	leaves and bark can be used to treat mild skin conditions

adding colour to the table

When you are serving food, it is beneficial to lay the table with care. The ambience in which you eat affects your receptiveness to the food's colour energy. The colour of the walls and quality of light in your dining area, the degree of comfort, the colour of the crockery, glassware and table settings – all combine to increase or lessen your appreciation of the food's colours.

In a canteen or fast-food outlet you may feel ill at ease seated at a plastic table under a harsh light. The flickering artificial light strips your food of its colour. The hard chair or bench on which you sit makes you want to get the meal over quickly – encouraging you, perhaps, to gulp down the food without chewing it carefully or appreciating its texture and aroma or the colour combinations it makes on the plate.

But in a comfortably furnished dining room – where your host has chosen a tablecloth that combines pleasingly with the colours of the walls, used lit candles to create an intimate and relaxing atmosphere, and selected plates, glasses and serving dishes that set off the quality of the food colours – you will find it much easier to take your time and savour the flavours, aromas and colour combinations of your meal.

CROCKERY

White plates contribute the perfect background to a riot of colour – for example, the varied greens and reds of a plateful of salad. Conversely, a red earthenware dish will enhance the appeal of a white mound of mashed potato or basmati rice. Consider serving a single-colour helping on a dish of a complementary colour – apricots on a blue plate or a green dish for a plateful of tomatoes.

FLOWER DISPLAY

A vase of freshly picked flowers adds a dash of colour, aroma and interest to mealtimes. Try to put fresh flowers in your dining area as often as possible, rather than simply reserving them for special occasions. You and your family will receive an energy boost from a lively orange and yellow display at breakfast time, say, raising your spirits and helping you prepare to go out and take on the world.

GARNISH

Add colour to a main meal with a side garnish – green lettuce, red tomato, a yellow slice of lemon, the blue-violet of aubergine pickle or a handful of berries.

DINING COLOUR

When preparing a table, consider the colours of the following combined with each other and with the food you are serving.

- decoration of dining area – walls, carpet, chairs, curtains, pictures

- table, tablecloth, placemats

- napkins and napkin rings

- salt and pepper dispensers

- any jars to be set on the table – for sauces and dressings, for example

- cutlery and crockery

- glass or other serving dishes and bowls

- glasses, decanters and jugs

- bottles containing drinks

- flower vases and displays

- lamps or candlesticks, coloured bulbs and candles

- effects of natural light and any outside view from the dining area

KITCHEN HERBS

If you do not have room for a herb garden, a few potted herbs will add colour and fragrance to your kitchen – and be on hand for cooking. If you do have a herb garden, pick a few plants and try using them in place of flowers for a dining-table display.

ALFRESCO DINING

If you have a garden with available space, consider investing in outdoor dining furniture. In summer, a restful evening meal or shady lunch outside enables your body – bathed in full-spectrum natural light and caressed by the aromas, sounds and varied hues of your garden – to gain maximum benefit from the colour energy of the meal.

colour, health and wellbeing

sensitivity to light

Colour is a powerful tool for protecting or restoring physical, mental and spiritual health. The visible rainbow colours are a form of energy, one part of the electromagnetic spectrum of radiation (see pages 10–11). If we understand how this energy can be harnessed, colour can be used to treat health and behavioural problems that derive from delicate imbalances in the body.

We receive colour energy through the skin as well as through the eyes (see page 12); every skin cell is sensitive to and responsive to light. The colour energy in light is drawn into organs, glands and body systems primarily through the body's seven main chakras or energy centres (see pages 112–13). Colour therapists understand illness and disease as an imbalance in the colour vibration specific to a body system, gland, organ or other part.

We can use treatment with coloured light, with colour-energized water or with powerful visualizations of colour to boost our immune and other body systems, soothe a stiff shoulder or other area of discomfort, ease depression or clarify

KEYS TO THE SPIRIT

If you are seeking to enhance a certain personal quality, use this checklist to see which colours can benefit you.

- **confidence** Yellow or orange will help you to attain your full spiritual stature.

- **self-discipline** Green, a source of balance and harmony, offers a way between the extremes of self-indulgence and asceticism.

- **contact with your higher self** Indigo or violet will clarify your thoughts and inspire you to lay aside what is standing between you and your spirit; magenta fosters spiritual yearning.

- **energy** Red will energize you to work with force and stamina.

- **creativity** Yellow improves alertness; indigo or violet fosters intuition.

- **communication** Orange unleashes the warmth and joy that are crucial to working successfully with others; blue harnesses communicative skills.

our thoughts. We can also use it to foster confidence or other qualities to which we aspire, or to dissolve aggression, banish anxiety and achieve spiritual peace.

LIGHT, SEASONS AND MOOD

Colour and light have profound effects on energy and mood. We perceive colours because light rays stimulate the cells in the eye to despatch nerve impulses to the brain's visual cortex (see page 12). Light-derived impulses also travel to the pineal gland, which determines sleep/wakefulness and other biorhythms, and the pituitary gland, which controls the release of hormones governing mood and many body functions.

COLOUR THERAPY IN THE ANCIENT WORLD

The healing power of coloured light was deeply respected by the ancient Egyptians. They poured liquids into coloured glass jars and bottles, then placed them in full daylight – the light, coloured by the container, filled the contents with colour energy. They also used coloured gems in healing: a person needing the healing vibration of a particular colour would ingest a powder made by grinding up a stone of that colour.

WINTER BLUES

If you live in a part of the world where the days are short and the weather is often gloomy in winter, lack of daylight can have an adverse effect on your moods and energy levels.

● Make sure that you go outside for around 30 minutes each day, to reap the benefit of the colours in full-spectrum daylight.

● Even in the worst weather, wrap up warm and try to take the air and drink in the light.

● When you are inside, sit or work close to a window. Pull up the blind, draw back the curtains and let in as much light as possible.

● The medical name for problems caused by lack of natural daylight in winter is seasonal affective disorder (SAD). Some sufferers have mild depression, others find it hard to function normally – for example, they often want to stay in bed, they avoid socializing and tend to overeat. SAD is thought to affect at least 10 per cent of people in northern Europe each year.

the energy of colour

Your body is surrounded by a field of electromagnetic energy called the aura, which both draws in and emits colour energy. Some people can see the aura as an egg-shaped sheath of colours around the body, and specialized Kirlian photography is said to be able to capture energy flow and reproduce the aura. We are all sensitive to one another's aura energy, although we cannot all see the aura itself.

Humans derive energy from light as well as from food. You have seven main energy centres or chakras on your body, arranged vertically between the base of your spine and the top of your skull. The chakras draw colour energy from full-spectrum light through the aura for the body's use. Each of the seven main chakras is attuned to one of the rainbow colours.

The theory of the chakras derives from esoteric forms of Hinduism. The word chakra comes from the Sanskrit *chakrum*, meaning wheel: the chakras are understood to be constantly spinning, and are sometimes likened to flowers endlessly opening and closing. There are said to be 88,000 chakras on the body, but the seven identified here are the most important. They are as follows: the base chakra, the sacral chakra, the solar plexus chakra, the heart chakra, the throat chakra, the brow chakra and the crown chakra.

SENSING THE AURA

We may sometimes have an immediate response to people based not on what they say or their physical appearance. We

YOUR BODY'S CHAKRAS

At the main chakras, your spiritual being and your physical body connect and interact. Each chakra governs a particular body system and organs (see page 114). Each is also associated with areas of self-expression and with physical, mental and spiritual qualities.

CHAKRA	COLOUR	GOVERNS
base (base of spine)	red	*physical survival, instinct, will, energy, vitality*
sacral (below the navel)	orange	*sexuality, hunger, social interaction*
solar plexus (above the navel)	yellow	*intellect, confidence, ego, self-control, optimism*
heart (central chest)	green	*balance, compassion for others and for self, love, self-security, forgiveness*
throat (throat)	blue	*creativity, speaking, self-expression*
brow (central forehead, 'third eye')	indigo	*intuitive thought, spiritual insight, self-knowledge*
crown (above the crown of the head)	violet	*higher spiritual knowledge, transcendence of self, access to deep inner divinity*

might feel uncomfortable around those individuals or disturbed by their presence, despite the fact that they may be saying kind words. At these times we may be detecting and responding to disturbances in those people's auras.

CONVINCE YOURSELF

Our knowledge of the chakras and the aura is derived from ancient wisdom – modern medical science does not accept their existence. Follow your own experience. As you progress in attuning your body to colour and become convinced of the restorative healing power of colour vibrations, the idea that we are surrounded by and emit a field of colour energy does not seem outlandish or improbable.

YOUR COLOURED CLOAK

A healthy aura operates as a protective shield, keeping negative energy at bay. As we develop greater sensitivity to our body's needs for colour energy, we will simultaneously ensure that the chakras are rich in their colour vibrations and that our aura is radiant. Strong in ourselves, we will be able to provide for the needs of those around us.

ETHERIC CHAKRA

Some therapists describe an eighth chakra, the etheric, which exists in the aura directly above the crown chakra at the top of the head. It is attuned to magenta, the colour that unites the two ends of the colour spectrum by blending violet and red.

THE AURA AND HEALTH

Balance is the key to health. An imbalance in the colours or energy of one chakra will have consequent effects on the energy and colours of the other chakras. Some colour healers can view the aura to diagnose energy imbalances and future physical ailments.

- **If your chakras are functioning well, receiving and distributing colour energy freely through your body, your physical, mental and spiritual health will be at an optimum level.**

- **When your chakras are healthy, your aura emits all the colours of the rainbow.**

- **If one or more of your chakras is blocked, or you are depleted in the colour energy associated with a particular chakra, then the aura will emit an unbalanced and muddy mixture of colours – often with a preponderance of blue and green. This unbalanced energy may eventually manifest itself as physical disease.**

colour you

Each of the main chakras governs a set of organs or a body system, and the colour vibration linked with a particular chakra benefits that chakra's associated organs and body system. These correspondences are your guide when you want to soothe pain or other symptoms using colour therapy.

COLOUR DIAGNOSIS

Colour changes in the body may be a sign of improved or of failing health. When a pink glow returns to the pale cheeks of a sick person, we know that person is well on the way to recovery, whereas if he or she is permanently flushed we suspect the existence of a circulatory problem or raised temperature. Both complementary healing and some forms of mainstream medicine use the colour of the skin as an indication of potential health problems. Possible skin diagnoses include yellow or orange skin signifying liver trouble; greying skin suggesting a depleted immune system; red, greasy skin showing heart or circulatory disorders, or fever; greenish skin indicating liver problems; and white patches showing kidney or liver trouble.

TONGUE COLOUR

Advocates of traditional Chinese medicine believe that the colour of the tongue – as well its texture, shape and coating – reveal detailed information about a patient's health. A very pale tongue indicates fever, whereas a dark-red or purple tongue is a sign of possible heart trouble.

CHAKRAS AND BODY SYSTEMS

Each main chakra in the body is associated with a particular colour and with a set of organs and a body system.

CHAKRA	COLOUR	ORGANS	BODY SYSTEM
base	red	*kidneys*	*muscular system*
sacral	orange	*reproductive organs and stomach*	*reproductive system*
solar plexus	yellow	*spleen, liver*	*digestive system*
heart	green	*heart*	*circulatory and nervous systems*
throat	blue	*throat, lungs*	*respiratory system*
brow	indigo	*eyes, ears, nose*	*skeletal system*
crown	violet	*brain*	*central nervous system (brain and spinal cord)*

ZODIAC COLOURS

Colour theory ascribes colours to each sign of the zodiac. An intense attraction to or need for a particular colour may be explained by your star sign.

- Aquarius (20 Jan–17 Feb)
  electric blue
- Pisces (18 Feb–19 Mar)
  turquoise, purple, green
- Aries (20 Mar–19 Apr)
  red
- Taurus (20 Apr–20 May)
  green
- Gemini (21 May–20 June)
  yellow
- Cancer (21 June–22 July)
  white, silver
- Leo (23 July–22 Aug)
  gold
- Virgo (23 Aug–22 Sept)
  light green, pale yellow
- Libra (23 Sept–22 Oct)
  blue, pink
- Scorpio (23 Oct–21 Nov)
  black, wine red
- Sagittarius (22 Nov–21 Dec)
  purple, magenta
- Capricorn (22 Dec–19 Jan)
  deep blue, deep green, black

TREATING COLOUR IMBALANCES IN THE BODY

There are many ways to use colour to soothe aches and pains, protect organs or glands, or boost a body system.

- wrap coloured scarves around an aching area, or on the part of the body where the organ is found
- drink water energized with the appropriate colour (see pages 120–21)
- rub colour-energized water on an affected area
- use coloured light treatments (see page 117)
- wear gemstones in the appropriate colour
- choose clothes in restorative colours
- redecorate part of your home in the colour you feel you need
- channel the appropriate colour (see pages 124–25) onto the affected part of the body
- use colour meditation to address areas of health concern (see pages 118–19)
- write colour affirmations (see page 125) for a particular part of the body

HEALTH CHECKLIST

If you want to improve one aspect of your physical, mental or spiritual health, consult the list below for helpful colours.

- if you suffer from poor concentration, consider using **yellow** or **violet**
- if you suffer from shortness of breath, consider using **blue**
- if you suffer from indigestion, consider using **yellow**
- if you suffer from feeling the cold, consider using **red**
- if you worry about or suffer from love problems, consider using **orange**
- if you are suffering from bereavement, consider using **pink** or **green**
- if you worry about or suffer from stress, consider using **green**
- if you suffer from persistent headaches, consider using **blue** or **violet**

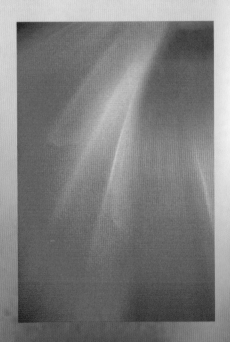

UNIVERSAL LIGHT

Observations of space indicate that the light in the universe is growing redder as it ages. Younger stars emit light at the **blue** end of the spectrum, but as stars grow older their light shifts towards **red**. As the number of older stars in the universe increases, the predominant colour of starlight moves from blue to red.

Light from very distant stars takes many millions of years to reach Earth — when today's astronomers observe a star, they see it as it was in the distant past, when the light began its long, long journey to Earth. In 2003 observations from the European Space Observatory telescope in Chile showed that 2.5 billion years ago, when the universe contained a larger number of younger stars, the light was predominantly blue.

light treatments

Our bodies are sensitive all over to light. The energy of different coloured lights can be absorbed through the skin as well as through the eyes (see page 12). In coloured-light treatment we use our knowledge of the healing and balancing effects of colours to ease troublesome states of mind or to soothe aches and pains.

Coloured-light treatments are given using the three primary colours of light: blue/violet, green and red/orange. Some treatments alternate a colour with its complementary hue in a pair that is energizing/soothing (for information on complementary colours, see page 14). This alternation boosts the beneficial effect of the treatment.

BATHING IN LIGHT

You can feel the benefits of different coloured-light treatments by 'bathing' the body all over in a particular colour. One way to do this is to combine a light treatment with a bath and to use coloured bath foam as well as coloured candles to achieve the required 'all-over' effect.

You can also use coloured bulbs or ordinary bulbs with coloured filters to direct light of the required colour onto the area of the chakra associated with the physical symptom or spiritual malaise that you are seeking to treat (see pages 112–14). Either remove clothing from the chakra you are focusing on or wear white garments – otherwise your clothes will filter the coloured light and your body will receive a light treatment that combines the original colour with that of your shirt or lower garments.

CHROMOTHERAPISTS

You can give yourself home treatment using coloured light, but it is usually advisable to visit a trained colour therapist or expert in coloured-light treatment, known as a chromotherapist, for a session. Chromotherapists are trained in the use of specialized equipment and can offer light therapy delicately attuned to your particular needs.

THE COLOUR OF LIGHT

Colour therapists often split the primary colours of light into their constituent parts: red, orange, violet, blue and green. Some add treatment with yellow light.

- **red light** (base chakra) Associated with vitality and strength; it can be used to treat lethargy and sometimes sexual impotence and (in addition to conventional medical treatment) to help with low blood pressure.

- **orange light** (sacral chakra) Associated with uplifting energy and happiness; orange light can be used to lift the spirits and improve a depressed state of mind.

- **violet light** (crown chakra) Boosts hope and a person's sense of inner worth and dignity; violet light treatment can be used to help people suffering from low self-esteem.

- **blue light** (throat chakra) Promotes relaxation and opening out; for this reason it is used with some success to ease the symptoms of asthma and migraine and may also help if you are suffering from insomnia.

- **green light** (heart chakra) Associated with balance; it is used to clear muddled thinking and as a purifying force.

- **yellow light** (solar plexus chakra) Associated with intellectual activity and critical thought; yellow light treatment has beneficial effects in treating mental confusion. Therapists also report success treating rheumatism and arthritis with yellow light.

colour meditation

Colour meditation draws on the healing power of the colour vibration that attracts your body or spirit. That colour vibration is present in the light around you and can be drawn through your aura and chakras into your body to support organs and body systems, feed your life force and elevate your spirit. Through the power of focused thought in meditation, you energize your body to receive the colour.

If you have a physical illness or discomfort associated with an organ or body system, use the list on page 114 to identify the relevant chakra and its colour. If you are suffering from low spirits or are trapped by emotions or bad habits, use the lists on pages 110, 112, 115, 117 and 121 to find the colour you need. Practise meditation using that colour. Persevere with the colour meditation until you feel its benefit. Try to begin the meditation with a trusting and receptive attitude, with readiness to receive guidance and healing.

The effectiveness of positive thinking can be enhanced by colour meditation. If you feel yourself slipping into negative, self-obsessed cycles of thought, use a burst of orange or yellow colour meditation to energize and clarify your thought processes, or a burst of violet colour meditation to strengthen your sense of connection with other people and your capacity to take pleasure in the happiness of others. Try a green colour meditation if you are seeking the middle way between extremes.

COLOUR AND THE POWER OF THOUGHT

The Buddhist tradition teaches that we are the product of what we think. The teachings of the Buddha in the ancient Dhammapada scripture indicate that those of us who think only of satisfying our own desires are storing up suffering for ourselves because we won't always get what we want. However, those who turn away from selfish thoughts find freedom in seeking the common good. Colour meditation can help us to find fulfilment and joy on the path of selfless service.

ORANGE COLOUR MEDITATION

Imagine that you are suffering from feelings of listlessness, you cannot summon up enthusiasm for your work, you feel reluctant to go out and meet friends. You decide to try a meditation in the colour orange.

Sit comfortably in a position that allows you most easily to forget your body. If you practise yoga and are supple, you may choose to sit in the lotus position – on the floor, with your back straight, your legs crossed and each foot resting on the opposing thigh with the sole turned upwards. Otherwise, sit in a straight-backed chair that encourages you to hold your spine erect and place your hands loosely on your thighs or along the arms of the chair, with palms turned upwards to indicate that you are receptive.

Imagine a sky of tender, delicate blue (complementary to orange), in which you see a sun of warming orange light. Alternatively, visualize a pool of peaceful blue on which you see floating a lotus of wonderful orange hue.

In this place, where you are entirely alone, the sun (or the lotus) manifests for you, makes its energy available for your healing. Its spinning orange centre fills your field of vision as it draws you in. A cloud of orange warmth envelops you. You are in the scene and yet remain within yourself – all is unity.

At the heart of the cloud, where you are now seated, is a place of healing and blessed calm. In that place, your body finds perfect rest and the restorative energies that it needs, while your spirit is emboldened to understand your true nature and your right task in life; inhibitions and anxieties melt away, and self-assurance and confidence return.

When you are ready, you emerge from the place of healing, grateful for its restorative energy. Open your eyes to return yourself to the day and its demands. Your confidence and vitality restored, you are ready to pass on the loving energy you have received through work, service and interaction with others.

coloured water treatments

When coloured light shines through a liquid, the liquid takes on some of the light's colour energy. One easy way to treat yourself with colour energy is to drink or bathe in colour-energized water.

COLOUR-ENERGY DRINKS

The time-honoured practice of drinking colour-energized water or milk to promote wellbeing – which was well-established among the ancient Egyptians and in the Indian Ayurvedic tradition – is returning to popularity.

Use liquid filled with the power of colour energy as a complementary treatment to ease minor conditions and physical pains or as a way of reinforcing spiritual qualities.

Start by filling a jug or tumbler made of coloured glass with mineral water or filtered tap water; alternatively, use clear glass wrapped in coloured plastic. Set the glassware in daylight for 20 minutes. It need not be sunny.

Sip the contents, focusing your mind on the spiritual qualities you wish to foster or the physical symptoms you want to ease.

ENERGIZED WATER AND ITS PROPERTIES

Violet is associated with modesty and will relieve a racing pulse or anxiety.

Indigo is associated with purity and will relieve aching eyes or headaches.

Blue is associated with calmness and honesty and will relieve a sore throat or nausea.

Green is associated with contentedness and will relieve a nasty shock and skin complaints.

Yellow is associated with clarity of expression and a positive outlook and will relieve constipation.

Orange is associated with good humour and an outgoing approach and will relieve indigestion.

Red is associated with passion and energy and will relieve exhaustion or poor circulation.

COLOURS OF LOVE

Are you are having a difficult time attracting a loved one or maintaining a relationship? Use colour energy to develop affection and other positive qualities in yourself or in your lover.

To develop qualities in yourself, use colour meditation, coloured water treatments or coloured light therapy – or simply surround yourself with the appropriate colour in your clothes, garden, home décor or diet.

Surround your lover with colour energy by using colour meditation while visualizing him or her, or by channelling colours onto him or her (see pages 124–25).

If you are at a stage that is 'in between' relationships, use pink energy to bolster your self-esteem, orange to develop self-confidence and blue to settle anxiety.

If your relationship suffers from a lack of honesty, use blue to heal rifts, recreate trust and encourage integrity.

If your relationships repeat damaging patterns of behaviour, use magenta for escape from past mistakes and for making a new start.

If your relationship is static or dying out, use red to recreate passion.

If your lover or partner refuses to discuss problems, use orange to help communication and blue to encourage straight speaking.

If past mistakes prevent you from being happy now, use pink to dissolve anger, magenta to escape the past and green to bolster hope.

COLOUR BATHING

A colour bath delivers an all-over treatment with soothing or uplifting energy. Mix the appropriate colour using food colourings or natural dyes. (Make sure you use non-staining varieties.)

- **indigo** or **blue** when you feel overheated, are seeking wisdom, are preparing for spiritual practice or are taking a few days' retreat from ordinary life

- **turquoise** or **green** when you feel tense, need to help others find a solution to a difficult problem or need to make a decision

- **yellow** when you feel muddled and unequal to a task or need to rediscover your cheerful outlook

- **orange** when you feel downhearted and need to restore your sense of humour and pleasure in everyday life

- **pink** when you feel ill at ease or need to forgive yourself or others

- **red** when you feel that your emotions are repressed or stifled, or your willpower is failing

breathing colours in and out

Colour breathing is a form of meditation that is given added power by the intensity of the subject's concentration on the physical process of inhaling and exhaling. You can use this practice to infuse yourself, body and spirit, with the healing power of colour.

SENDING COLOUR ENERGY

You can perform colour breathing for yourself or on behalf of another person: when you are intending to direct colour energy towards another person, hold them in the full light of your attention for a few moments before starting the breathing exercise.

COLOUR BREATHING EXERCISE

Find a comfortable place to sit (see page 119). Breathe in deeply, holding each breath for a few moments before breathing out gently, noticing the sensations associated with each part of your inhalation and exhalation. Establish a pattern of deep, restful breathing.

Incorporate the colour you need to complete the exercise: use the lists on pages 110, 112, 114–15, 117 and 121 when making your colour choice.

in a state of perfect health, surrounded by a glowing aura that reflects the balance of colour energies you contain.

CHANNELLING COLOUR WITH THE HANDS

You can channel colour through your hands onto your own body or onto someone else's body.

Ask the person to lie down on a divan or bed and channel colour healing onto the affected part of his or her body.

Prepare carefully: wash gently, try to settle your thoughts and breathing, and envisage yourself – particularly your hands – as a conduit for healing. Find a comfortable seated position.

When you have summoned the colour energy you need, hold your hands over the part of the body that needs healing.

Feel the energy passing through your fingers onto and through the skin, bringing healing energy to every cell and tissue. If you or your subject are wearing clothing over that area, it should be white or neutral in colour.

COLOUR AFFIRMATIONS

When writing an affirmation we call on the qualities we desire for ourselves – for example, by writing 'I am confident of my ability to deal with any setback', 'I am at peace with myself' or 'I honour my intuition and my ability to be creative'. Affirmations energize and reinforce our better selves, keeping self-doubt and lethargy at bay. Colour affirmations summon the qualities of particular colours into our lives.

MAKING AN AFFIRMATION

Write your affirmation on a small card or piece of paper that you can view everyday on your desk or carry around with you in your pocket or handbag.

- if you feel upset, your affirmation might be 'Using **green** energy I will find security and balance.'

- if you feel afraid, your affirmation might be 'By embracing **red** energy I will go forward with confidence in myself and without fear.'

- if you feel overexcited or unable to settle or relax, your affirmation might be '**Blue** energy calms me, allowing me to accept my lot and proceed with trust.'

- if you feel daunted by a difficult job, your affirmation might be 'Through **indigo** I develop my intuition and creativity.'

PICTURE CREDITS AND ACKNOWLEDGMENTS

KEY: **a**=above, **b**=below, **r**=right, **l**=left, **c**=centre.

1 *ph* Debi Treloar; 2 *ph* Caroline Arber; 3 *ph* Sandra Lane/cushion from Graham & Green; 4–5 *ph* William Lingwood; 6 *ph* Andrea Jones; 10–11 © Goodshoot; 12–13 © Stockbyte; 15 Courtesy of the Color Wheel Company; 16–17 *ph* Dan Duchars; 18–19 *ph* Andrea Jones; 20–21 *ph* Pia Tryde; 22–23 *ph* Craig Fordham; 26–27 *ph* David Montgomery; 30–31 *ph* Debi Treloar/Mark and Sally of Baileys Home & Garden's house in Herefordshire; 32–33 *ph* Polly Wreford/Marie-Hélène de Taillac's pied-à-terre in Paris; 34 *ph* Polly Wreford; 35 *ph* James Merrell; 36 *ph* Debi Treloar/Susan Cropper's family home in London, www.63hlg.com; 37 *ph* Polly Wreford; 38–39 *ph* Debi Treloar; 40 *ph* Catherine Gratwicke/Ellis Flyte's house in London; 41 *ph* Catherine Gratwicke; 42l *ph* Polly Wreford; 42–43 *ph* Catherine Gratwicke; 44 *ph* James Merrell; 45a *ph* Christopher Drake; 45b *ph* Polly Wreford/House Stylist Clare Nash's former home in London; 48–49 *ph* Alan Williams/Richard Oyarzarbal's apartment in London designed by Urban Research Laboratory; 51 *ph* Debi Treloar/Debi Treloar's family home in northwest London; 52–53 *ph* Chris Everard/An apartment in Paris designed by architects Guillaume Terver and Fabienne Couvert of cxt sarl d'architecture; 53r *ph* Polly Wreford/Jo Plismy, Gong; 54b ph Debi Treloar/Ian Hogarth's family home; 54a–55a *ph* Ray Main/Seth Stein's house in London; 55b *ph* Debi Treloar/Designed by Sage Wimer Coombe Architects, New York (now Sage and Coombe Architects); 56l *ph* Debi Treloar/David & Macarena Wheldon's house in London designed by Fiona McLean; 56–57 *ph* Debi Treloar/Family home in Bankside, London; 57r *ph* James Merrell/Sally Butler's house in London; 58 *ph* Daniel Farmer; 59 inset *ph* Daniel Farmer; 59 *ph* Alan Williams/Owner of Gloss, Pascale Bredillet's own apartment in London; 60–61 *ph* Catherine Gratwicke/Bryan Purcell, an artist living in New York; 61r *ph* David Brittain; 62 *ph* Andrew Wood/Rosa Dean & Ed Baden-Powell's apartment in London, designed by Urban Salon Ltd; 63r *ph* Debi Treloar/Architect Simon Colebrook's home in London; 64l *ph* Polly Wreford/Emma Greenhill's London home; 64–65 *ph* Jan Baldwin/David Gill's house in London; 66l *ph* Andrew Wood/Nello Renault's loft in Paris; 66r *ph* Andrew Wood/Gabriele Sanders' apartment in New York; 67 *ph* Chris Everard/the London apartment of the Sheppard Day Design Partnership; 68 *ph* Catherine Gratwicke/the brownstone in New York of Bonnie Young, director of global sourcing and inspiration at Donna Karan International; 69 *ph* James Merrell; 70 *ph* Ray Main/Seth Stein's house in London; 71 *ph* Alan Williams/Alannah Weston's house in London designed by Stickland Coombe Architecture; 74 *ph* Francesca Yorke; 75 *ph* Andrea Jones; 76–77 *ph* Melanie Eclare/Daphne Shackleton's garden in Co. Cavan, Ireland; 77r *ph* Melanie Eclare; 78a & b *ph* Andrea Jones; 78–79 *ph* Caroline Arber/Rosemary Titterington at Iden Croft Herbs, Staplehurst, Kent; 81 *ph* Andrea Jones; 81a Blooms of Bressingham; 82–83 *ph* Andrea Jones/Rowden Gardens; 83r *ph* Melanie Eclare/Elspeth Thompson's garden in south London; 84–85 *ph* Melanie Eclare/Sticky Wicket wildlife garden near Dorchester, designed and created by Peter and Pam Lewis; 86l *ph* Pia Tryde; 86r–87l *ph* Melanie Eclare; 87ac *ph* Steve Painter; 87br *ph* Melanie Eclare; 88 *ph* Francesca Yorke; 89 *ph* Pia Tryde; 90l *ph* Pia Tryde; 90–91 *ph* Stephen Robson; 91ar *ph* Stephen Robson; 91br *ph* Pia Tryde; 94–95 *ph* William Lingwood; 95a *ph* Vanessa Davies; 95c *ph* Pia Tryde; 95b *ph* Nicky Dowey; 96l *ph* William Lingwood; 96–97 *ph* Debi Treloar; 98b *ph* Peter Cassidy; 98–99 & 99bc *ph* Francesca Yorke; 99ar *ph* Peter Cassidy; 100a *ph* Alan Williams; 100bl *ph* Martin Brigdale; 100br *ph* Ian Wallace; 101a *ph* Peter Cassidy; 101b *ph* Craig Robertson; 102 *ph* Jean Cazals; 102l inset *ph* Pia Tryde; 102r inset *ph* Caroline Hughes; 103l *ph* Peter Cassidy; 103r *ph* Francesca Yorke; 103b *ph* Alan Williams; 104al *ph* Peter Cassidy; 104ar *ph* Pia Tryde; 104b *ph* Francesca Yorke; 105ar *ph* Peter Cassidy; 105bl & bc *ph* Caroline Hughes; 105br *ph* Alan Williams; 106–107 *ph* Debi Treloar; 111 inset *ph* Jan Baldwin; 113 © Science Photo Library; 115 insets *ph* Polly Wreford; 119 inset *ph* Polly Wreford; 120 inset *ph* Jan Baldwin; 121 inset *ph* Emma Lee; 122 *ph* Polly Wreford; 124–125 insets *ph* Polly Wreford.

BUSINESS CREDITS

Baileys Home & Garden
The Engine Shed
Station Approach
Ross-on-Wye
Herefordshire HR9 7BW
01989 563015
www.baileyshomeand
garden.com
Pages 30–31.

Bonnie Young
*Director of global sourcing
and inspiration, Donna
Karan International*
+1 212 228 0832
Page 68.

Bressingham Plant Centre
Bressingham
Diss
Norfolk IP22 2AB
01831 280058
Page 81a.

Dive Architects
A009 The Jam Factory
19 Rothsay Street
London SE1 4UF
020 7407 0955
www.divearchitects.com
Pages 56–57.

Ellis Flyte
Fashion designer
020 7431 7560 (f)
Pages 40.

Emma Greenhill
egreenhill@freenet.co.uk
Page 64l.

Fabienne Couvert
*Guillaume Terver
cxt sarl d'architecture*
12 rue Saint Fiacre
75002 Paris
France
+33 1 55 34 9850
www.couverterver-
architectes.com
Pages 52–53.

Fiona McLean
McLean Quinlan Architects
2a Bellevue Parade
London SW17 7EQ
020 8767 1633
www.mcleanquinlan.com
Page 56l.

Gloss Ltd
Portobello Green Arcade
Unit 24
281 Portobello Road
London W10 5TZ
020 8969 4653
Page 59.

Gong
142 Portobello Road
London W11 2DZ
020 7565 4162
www.gong.co.uk
Page 53r.

Graham & Green
7 Elgin Crescent
London W11 2JA
020 7727 4594
www.grahamand
green.com
Page 3.

Iden Croft Herbs
Staplehurst
Kent TN12 0DH
01580 891 432
www.herbs-uk.com
Pages 78–79.

Liminal
+47 9309 4515
www.liminal-design.com
Jacket inset left centre.

Littman Goddard Hogarth
61 Courtfield Gardens
London SW5 0NQ
www.lgh-architects.co.uk
Page 54b.

Peter & Pam Lewis
*Garden design, restoration
and management*
Sticky Wicket
Buckland Newton
Dorset DT2 7BY
01300 345 476
Pages 84–85.

Rebecca & Bryan Purcell
Artists
436 Fort Washington Avenue
New York, NY 10033
USA
Pages 60–61.

Rowden Gardens
Brentor
Nr Tavistock
Devon PL19 0NG
01822 810275
Pages 82–83.

Sage and Coombe
Architects
205 Hudson Street
Suite 1002
New York, NY 10013
USA
+1 212 226 9600
www.sageandcoombe.com
Page 55b.

Seth Stein Architects
15 Grand Union Centre
West Row
Ladbroke Grove
London W10 5AS
020 8968 8581
www.sethstein.com
Pages 54a–55a, 70.

Sheppard Day Design
020 7821 2002
Page 67.

Simon Colebrook, Architect
Douglas Stephen Partnership
140–142 St John Street
London EC1V 4UB
020 7336 7884
www.dsparchictecture.co.uk
Page 63r.

**Stickland Coombe
Architecture**
258 Lavender Hill
London SW11 1LJ
020 7924 1699
www.sticklandand
coombe.com
Page 71.

Susan Cropper
www.63hlg.com
Page 36.

Urban Research Lab
Lime Wharf
Vyner Street
London E2 9DJ
020 8709 9060
www.urbanresearchlab.com
Pages 48–49.

Urban Salon Ltd
Ayres Street
London E2 9DJ
020 7357 8800
www.urbansalon
architects.com
Page 62.

index

USEFUL ADDRESSES

www.colourtherapyhealing.com *A colour therapy resource.*

www.iac-colour.co.uk International Association of Colour. *Founded by colour therapy pioneer Theo Gimbel.*

freespace.virgin.net/hygeia.north Hygeia College in the North. *Colour therapy courses in the UK.*

www.holistics.co.uk *An holistic healing resource.*